Goddard Binkley

The Expanding Self

The Alexander Technique encourages growth and development of the self in all of life's activities. This process is uniquely illustrated in Goddard Binkley's diaries which describe just how fundamentally ons's use of the self can change. His detailed diary entries of his lessons with F. M. Alexander are the most extensive record of how the Technique's originator taught. This diary, which forms the main part of the book, is preceded by the story of Binkley's early life and is followed by his notes and observations on Alexander's teacher training course. His growth and "expansion" encompasses all aspects of his being—not least his development in painting and sculpture which he describes as well as his meetings with significant figures of the British art world in the 1950s.

Goddard Binkley was born in 1920 in Chicago. During his studies towards a Ph.D. in Sociology at the New School for Social Research, New York, he started having lessons in the Alexander Technique. Considering training as an Alexander teacher he went to London in 1951 to have lessons with F. M. Alexander. He joined Alexander's teacher training course in 1953 and qualified in 1957. He taught the Technique in New York from 1959 to 1971 and in Chicago from 1971 to 1981. He ran his own teacher training course from 1975 to 1981. He then moved to Paris where he ran a training course until he died in 1987 from a rare disease of the bone marrow.

Goddard Binkley

THE EXPANDING SELF

How the Alexander Technique
Changed My Life

STAT▪Books

First published September 1993 by

STAT Books

The books division of
The Society of Teachers of the Alexander Technique
20 London House
266 Fulham Road
London SW10 9EL
Great Britain

ISBN 0–9519304–3–5 Hardback
The Expanding Self
How The Alexander Technique Changed My Life

British Library Cataloguing-in-Publication Data
A catalogue record for his book is available from the British Library.

Photoset in Adobe Goudy and lay-out by CF Top Publishing, Denmark.
Printed and bound by Redwood Books, Trowbridge, Wiltshire

One-third of the income from the sales of this book will be donated to
The F. Matthias Alexander Trust
Registered Charity no. 802 856

2 4 6 8 10 9 7 5 3 1

CONTENTS

Publisher's acknowledgement

The publication of this book
was made possible by a
generous donation from

The Tory Family Foundation

to

The F. Matthias Alexander Trust

A NOTE ON THE TEXT

The transcription follows the last version Binkley left behind of his type-script, dated October 1985, two years before his premature death. Although it was prepared for publication, allowance must be made for the fact that it is an unfinished work.

For general convenience misspellings have been corrected and punctuation, capitalisation and the usage of often repeated words have been standardised. American spelling, where it occurs, has been retained. Italics have been used to indicate names, titles, etc. as is common practice in printed works, but all other italics are original to the work. Where Binkley has added italics to Alexander's text this has been indicated. Square brackets within a quotation denote Binkley's comments. Square brackets outside quotations signify my emendations.

Changes in wording have only been done in a few cases to eradicate unnecessary ambiguities and I have relied on one of Binkley's earlier drafts to ensure his meaning has been preserved. The diary entry describing the London fog has been added from an earlier draft. Some alterations have also been made to the quotations from F. M. Alexander's books to ensure that they are *ipsissima verba*. The abbreviations and editions of F. Matthias Alexander's books which Binkley refers to are as follows:

MSI	*Man's Supreme Inheritance*
	Chaterson Ltd, third edition, 1946
CCCI	*Constructive Conscious Control of the Individual*
	Chaterson Ltd, eighth edition, 1946
UoS	*The Use of the Self*
	Chaterson Ltd, third edition, 1946
UCL	*The Universal Constant in Living*
	Chaterson Ltd, third edition, 1946

Such annotations as Ian MacFadyen and I have judged to be of use and interest to the reader are marked with a number and are placed at the end of the book lest they should distract the reader. These footnotes are intended to provide concise and relevant information to names, places and books which were part of Binkley's world, interests and thought. Many of these will be familiar to readers of Binkley's generation but younger or more distant readers may find them useful to appreciate the life and times in which these diaries were written.

Jean M. O. Fischer
Leeds, July 1993

Illustrations

The illustrations are between pages 82 and 83

Goddard Binkley in 1986, outside Paris (Courtesy of Joanna Binkley)

Tom Mott, Bill (P. E.) Williams and Goddard Binkley in St. James Park, London, c. 1953. (Photo by Anthony Spawforth).

Untitled, black crayon sketch of girl by Goddard Binkley, similar to the one exhibited at the Artists of Chelsea Exhibition, May 1953 (Courtesy of Joanna Binkley)

House and Barns, oil on canvas, exhibited at Artists of Chelsea Exhibition, May 1953 (Courtesy of Joanna Binkley)

F. M. Alexander, bust by Goddard Binkley, 1953 (Courtesy of Joanna Binkley)

Woman Sitting, sculpture, 1956 (Courtesy of Joanna Binkley)

F. Matthias Alexander teaching, photos from the article "The Man who helped Sir Stafford Cripps", *Leader Magazine*, 11 December 1948

Ashley Place and Westminster Cathedral, London, (© Aerofilms, published in *Illustrated London News*, 25 February 1950)

FOREWORD

It is a great pleasure to me to be asked to write a foreword to this book. I have been hoping to see it in print ever since I first read the manuscript in 1956.

I knew Goddard Binkley from the time that he first came to Ashley Place to have private lessons from Alexander. I worked with him when he entered the training course, and after Alexander's death, in 1955, I completed his training and gave him his certificate. We remained firm friends for the rest of his life.

He showed me the diary in 1956 and I was struck at once by its vivid portrayal of Alexander and the detailed account of his lessons. He had a true Boswellian gift; just as James Boswell brought Dr. Johnson to life so that it seemed as though we could all share in the great man's friendship, the warmth of his personality, and his wisdom, so Goddard has performed a similar miracle here.

Those of us who knew Alexander, and who were taught and trained by him, can vouch for the authenticity of the portrait that Goddard paints. We can hear the familiar inflections of his voice and his whole manner of expression in the words that are reported.

I have often read parts of this diary to the students on our training course and they have been fascinated. It has served to answer their repeated questions; "What was Alexander really like?" and "What was it like to have a lesson from him?" Now these answers can be shared by a wider audience.

Although I have so long wished that this diary could appear in print, I must point out that it can be no substitute for the study of Alexander's own writings. There he sets out his teaching in unequivocal terms that will repay the most careful reading.

Of course Goddard also reveals much about himself and his personal life in the pages of his diary. And whether you empathize with him or not you will certainly be led to see the effect that his study and practice of the Technique had upon his life and character. I think that you will find it to be a fascinating story and one from which there is much to learn.

Personally I am grateful to all those involved in the eventual publication of this book and I think that Goddard would have been more than happy to see his hopes and intentions finally realized. I hope that you will appreciate it as much as I do.

Walter H. M. Carrington
London, July 1993

This Book is Dedicated to

F. Matthias Alexander

And my other teachers—

Walter Carrington
Margaret Goldie
Peter Scott
Philomene Barr
Norris Barr

My fellow students
in the Teacher Training Course in London,
at 16 Ashley Place and 5 Bainbridge Street,
from 1953 to 1957

And to the late Frank Pierce Jones

Acknowledgements

I am deeply grateful to the following persons, all of whom contributed in various ways to the writing of this book.

Walter Carrington was the first to read the diary after I gathered the courage to show it to him when still a student in the training course. He said it was "First rate!" In correspondence during many succeeding years, he increasingly encouraged me to publish it in some form or another. His most recent advice was to "keep it simple!"—good advice, which I hope to have carried out.

Margaret Goldie, I wish to record here, generously gave me weekly lessons during my final training year in London (and some in later years). Much as I appreciated those lessons then, I appreciate them even more now, thirty years later. I also appreciated her relationship to Alexander, and so I was particularly anxious to show her the diary. She read it with great critical care and made a page by page list of suggestions and changes concerned mostly with biographical details (of F. M.) and certain teaching terms, e.g., not "orders," but "guiding orders."

Frank Pierce Jones, with whom I enjoyed a stimulating correspondence from 1958 to the time of his fatal illness in the mid-70s, read the diary after I mailed him a copy in December 1959. In a January letter, he wrote: "I was fascinated to read the diary you kept of your lessons with F. M. It is a valuable document. I doubt that it would interest a publisher at the present time, but I might be mistaken." I found these words enormously encouraging.

Elizabeth Dipple, Professor of graduate English at Northwestern University and an experienced Alexander pupil, read and edited a later version of the diary incorporating entries from my journal. I am especially indebted to her for her emphatic suggestions as to how the book should be organized with the diary as the centerpiece. It was relatively clear sailing after that.

John R. Mahon, a publicist and pupil, made helpful suggestions concerning continuity.

Finally, as regards editing, my sister, Anne Ozbekhan, helped clarify instances of awkward syntax and doubtful meaning.

In addition to the above, I wish to express my thanks to some pupils who read the diary and were critically helpful in their comments: Eric McCormack, O. S. B., Edward Maisel, Joan Potter, Kirk Renor, Christine Heatherington, Belle Snyder, Michael Allswang, Sheila Sirey, Diana Smith, Gail Quillman, Joan Bauman and Denise Lemoine.

My former wife, Margrit I. Binkley, was with me through the diary and training course years and many beyond, attending always to the needs of a growing Joanna, Jessica, David and Mark. So special thanks to her; and, finally, also to my former student, Micheline Valissant, for her love and encouragement and the existence of Caroline.

Introduction

When I met F. Matthias Alexander (July 1951) I was already interested in becoming a teacher of the Technique. The preceding year I had read his books, taken lessons with a teacher in New York, and I was philosophically in tune with the idea. The lessons had also effectively rid me of a more or less painful and depressive psycho-physical condition that had started early in my life. This was a great change in my life, but I was aware that it was an incidental outcome of lessons in the Technique which teaches the natural and proper use of the self. My experience demonstrates the truth of Alexander's contention that "the first principle in all training, from the earliest years of child life, must be on a conscious plane of co-ordination, re-education, and readjustment, which will establish a normal kinæsthesia." (*Man's Supreme Inheritance*, p. 42)

My lessons with Alexander began in the summer of 1951 and ended in the summer of 1953, from the 82nd to the 84th year of his life. After most of these lessons I wrote down from memory what to me were the more important and interesting of his comments and instructions. It was easy to recall his words. Even if I waited until the evening to write them down I could hear him speaking as though he were still standing beside me. This "Alexander diary" (referred to hereafter as the diary) makes up most of Part II.

Part I is an autobiographical narrative covering some events in my life prior to the lessons with Alexander. It also includes dated excerpts from my journal, a nine-year record of various thoughts, feelings and experiences from 1948 to 1957 (the year I finished the training course and went back to America). Some of the journal material has also gone into Part II.

In June of 1953, with Alexander's blessings, I entered the teacher training course. From time to time I made notes of our activities and experiences. These notes make up Part III, which also includes a few journal entries.

I conclude the book with an epilogue, a brief narrative to bring the reader more or less up to the present time.

Goddard Binkley
Paris 1986

Part I

BACK TROUBLE, DOUBT AND DEPRESSION

My First Thirty Years

1920–1950

From the age of three I grew up in Glencoe, a suburb on Chicago's North Shore. There are five in our family. I have a twin brother and a sister two years older. My father, who died six years after we moved to Glencoe, was prominent in the coal business. My mother followed her interests in music, painting and photography, and learned how to manage the modest estate left by my father. My brother turned out to be an architect, my sister a writer, and I, a teacher of the Alexander Technique.

At age eight, I was badly burned. Some older boys across the street had filled an old oil drum with water, plugged it up tight, set it on bricks and built a fire underneath. I played the fireman and fed scraps of wood and dead branches into the fire. Suddenly, my sister, watching with friends, cried, "Something's going to happen!" Everybody ran, except me—I continued feeding the fire.

The next thing I knew I was sprawled flat on my back looking up at the oil drum floating in the air. I spent three days in the hospital. The doctor said the sweater I wore probably saved my life.

When I was twelve, I began to have back trouble. The first sign of it came as I was sitting at the piano, practising. A sudden sharp pain made me fall to one side. I slowly straightened myself up and felt nothing, but it happened again a few days later and then more frequently. Soon I was feeling pain right after getting into bed at night and then again on getting up in the morning.

During the day, my back would tire easily, then start to ache, the ache turning into pain. About this time I noticed that I was looking up at people from underneath my eyebrows. In the eighth grade I went out for football but quickly discovered my back couldn't take the jolting. I made the track team, putting the shot and throwing the discus—movements which, I realize now, tended to induce a "head-up" posture.

Moving into the ninth and then the tenth grade at the New Trier High School and the back pains getting worse, my parents (my mother remarried) sought out one of Chicago's foremost orthopaedic doctors, Dr. Emil Hauser.

Dr. Hauser said I had a severe lumbar lordosis (sway back) with the muscles in spasm, overcontracted, causing the pain. He put me in Passavant Hospital for a week's bed rest and daily back massage. Then to the cast room, where he asked me to stand as tall as I could. As I kept standing tall, he wrapped the wet plaster strips around my torso. As the plaster hardened, I realized I was standing in a different way, and without effort. I felt a good two inches taller, and when I walked out of the hospital I felt buoyed up, as if I were walking under water. Dr. Hauser said I must wear the cast for four months (the second semester of my sophomore year) and, in addition, exercise for five minutes and rest ten minutes lying down, each hour of the school day.

To accommodate this rigorous schedule and keep up the school work, I enrolled in the North Shore School of Concentration. The director was Dr. Swedelius, a large man with a deep voice. The school consisted of three rooms on the upper floor of his home. He taught all subjects except English and American History. He specialized in preparing New Trier seniors for their College Board exams. There were five such students besides myself.

Discipline was enforced by an always visible two feet of rubber hose lying on his desk. He had to use it only once, on all of us, with a whack across the back. He was, without a doubt, an extraordinary teacher. Whatever the subject, Math, Physics or Latin, he took away the cobwebs and made things clear. I did my exercises in a hallway and rested on an army cot he set up in one of the rooms.

As the days and weeks passed, I did not find the cast a hindrance; indeed, my movements were facilitated by the "lift" of the cast, and, because I was no longer pulling myself into a slump, I got a different view of my surroundings. Gradually I felt and could partly see the newly developed muscles under the top edge of the cast and lost the feeling of being propped up by it. When, finally, the cast was removed, there seemed to be little change in my new upright posture. But I was fitted with a steel-ribbed corset to wear during the day. I continued with rest and exercise periods, but only several times a day.

The next three years I spent at two private schools: a year at Cranbrook, near Detroit, and two at Lake Forest Academy, just a twenty-minute drive from Glencoe. Somewhere around the middle of those three years, I experienced some kind of intellectual awakening—things got a lot easier for me. My first year at New Trier had been abysmal, getting all but failing grades, though I had worked reasonably hard. But I always had the feeling I was trying to push a stone wall, getting nowhere. Arriving at Cranbrook, I voluntarily repeated the second year of two subjects because I didn't feel sufficiently grounded in them. This delayed my secondary school graduation by a year; but the prospect of that didn't seem important. My grades improved markedly, and, above all, I felt I was looking around and seeing things clearly for the first time. I took a real interest in my subjects, Chemistry in particular—I spent hours in the library reading popular books on chemistry. I loved jazz or swing, and the following year at Lake Forest Academy I joined the concert orchestra and the jazz band, playing the drums in both. My brother and I were day-students at LFA. Living at home, I would often study into the small hours of the morning. During those hours I began writing poems, a practice which grew over the next seven years. I stayed away from football because of my back but put the shot and threw the discus on the track team.

When my brother graduated, I had one more year to go. I graduated with honors, taking prizes in Chemistry and German.

On one of those nights studying into the early morning hours, I had an experience which has never repeated itself. It might have been what I've heard called a satori experience. I was sitting at my desk when I was suddenly seized with an oceanic sensation of knowing and understanding and comprehending the whole of life.

It was like a flowing together of me and the universe! I was overwhelmed! I got up from my chair and lay on my bed. Thoughts and images flooded into my head. I had to write them down, as they came to me:

The mind of man. Emotions. Dig under humanity, feel its plight. Grasp with your mind, your emotions, everything in your power. Envelope and understand man. Don't ignore things. Don't progress through life in a light color, with weak understanding, petty ideals or conclusions. Form a basis and build from that basis. As you build, spread your arms and grasp with your hands the actions, motives, emotions, ideals and aspirations of man! Understand intellectually and emotionally. Don't fly over the sea of life. Swim under, on the very bottom. For only on the bottom will you find the basis of all things, material and spiritual. Be aware of other people, read them, understand them. With understanding, Life can be understood. Spread your mind and grasp with reason all things. Be open! Don't close your eyes! Don't close your mind!

I had decided to study medicine and enter the University of Chicago as a pre-med student but gave in to the wishes of my stepfather, an ardent Californian, and registered at Stanford University. I spent the last couple of weeks before going to California recovering from an appendectomy which was supposed to cure a chronic feeling of wanting to belch, but it did not. My brother was going to the University of California after spending a year in Paris studying painting with my sister.

My back at this time was still much improved. I still wore the corset and exercised several times a week. But my back tired easily, and I had to be careful lifting heavy objects. What constantly reminded me of the vulnerability of my back was simply washing my hands in a wash basin—though slight, it was always a strain. Even though Dr. Hauser gave me all the benefit of his medical knowledge and good judgment, (bless him for not operating!), he didn't know—other than putting me in a plaster cast—how to get me to *stop my pulling down and collapsing*, which would continue to be my general psycho-physical orientation towards life at least for the next ten years. It was obvious, though not to me, that I was fighting a losing battle.

Stanford turned out to be a disaster. I had two roommates, both of whom I liked but saw little of because I was seldom there. After a few days I hated the university, the campus and all the students! I was in mental anguish. Speaking to no one, except my roommates, I struggled with my thoughts and feelings. I couldn't read a sentence, much less concentrate on my studies, without tormenting thoughts thrashing about in my head. It seemed as though life itself were a threat to my existence. I cut most of my classes and tried to catch up by all-night vigils in a Palo Alto hotel. I felt a compelling need to be alone and out of the class room. I wrote home, saying, "I need to take stock of things." Where could I go? I saw a travel agent, and she said, "Carmel!" I packed my bags and left without saying a word to anyone, though a few days later after settling in Carmel, I returned for a long talk with the Dean and the resident psychologist, and took an official leave which would enable me to return if and when I changed my mind.

In Carmel I rented a room over a garage amongst widely scattered bungalow-type houses on a pine tree covered hillside overlooking the sea. I took walks on the beach, wrote poems and letters. I made friends with a few shop owners and got a weekend job washing dishes in a dairy bar. I rented a small upright piano. Though, in the past, I had never worked hard or consistently at the piano, I was now having serious thoughts about being a composer. For some time I had been composing little pieces at the piano, and now I tried to write them down. On a few weekends my brother came down for a visit from Berkeley, and I went up to see him. I remember the eucalyptus trees. When Christmas-time came, I went home by train, planning to return after the New Year. But, counselled by my sister, I enrolled at the American Conservatory of Music as a full-time student. But by the end of term in June I knew I had not the dedication and probably not the talent for serious work in music. Enthusiastic at first, my effort was distinctly half-hearted. I was nagged by the thought that I should be getting on with the serious work of college and then medical school. When September came, I was a student at Hamilton College, near Utica, New York.

The Hamilton campus was on a beautiful elm tree shrouded hilltop above the Mohawk Valley. At the time it was a men's college of about 300 students. I joined a fraternity, became a member of Hamilton's regionally famous choir and, in spite of my vulnerable back, but armored by the corset, I played freshman football. Except for one brilliant afternoon at practice, my playing was unexceptional. Our coach was Forrest Evashevski, the great blocking back for Tom Harmon on Michigan's 1940 team and who went on, after Hamilton, to win fame as a coach at Iowa and Northwestern. That afternoon I was playing left tackle on the second string scrimmaging with the first string. On defense, I decided to stop doing what I was accustomed to do, namely, hunker down low and make myself an immovable object. Instead, I kept my head up to watch who got the ball and where it was going. Meanwhile I side-stepped or gave ground to my charging opponent and tackled the ball carrier each time he headed my way. This went on for play after play. The guys were amazed at my new agility and prowess. So was I. It seemed like somebody else, not me, who was making those tackles. When practice was over, Evashevski walked all the way to the locker room with his arm around my shoulder praising my performance. But it didn't happen again. I don't quite know why. I suspect that for a few hours that afternoon I had put myself in what Alexander called a position of mechanical advantage or something close to it. I had lengthened, expanded and strengthened my body by keeping my head up to watch the ball runner rather than squat down low, pull my head back, and watch my opponent.

In my second year at Hamilton I was having growing doubts about myself, the start of what I later called a doubting disease, I was afraid of the future and more and more often depressed. What did I really want to do in life? I didn't know. But what really bothered me was that I couldn't see myself doing anything and being successful at it. My thoughts of medicine were now giving way to thoughts of being a writer. I devoted larger and larger portions of my time to writing poems, and reading Hemingway,[1] Sherwood Anderson,[2] and Huxley.[3] Hamilton's magazine, *The Continental*, published two of my poems, and I made the drawing for the cover. The war in Europe was two years old and that year Pearl Harbor was America's Christmas present. In the spring I joined the V-7 program of the United States Naval Reserve. The finality of that was somehow relieving: I wouldn't have to worry about what I was going to do with my life for quite a while.

Now the summer of '42, I took a six-week intensive course in Physics at Northwestern, wrote poems whenever I was alone at a table or a desk— many at Evanston's Cooley's Cupboard and NU's Scott Hall with the noise and the students, which I found stimulating—and saw friends, old and new. Most of the time, these years, I was in love or falling in love. But, for me, the special thing I did that summer was to take an intensive ten-day seminar in General Semantics given by its founder, Alfred Korzybski, and to read, and re-read, his book, *Science and Sanity: an Introduction to Non-Aristotelian Systems.*[4]

General Semantics had a distinctly purifying, immensely stimulating, and thoroughly therapeutic effect on my feelings, thoughts and general attitude towards life and the world. [5]

I looked and listened with rapt attention as Korzybski talked and gesticulated, absorbed in his every expression, gesture and movement. He constantly illustrated his concepts with diagrams and symbols and, sometimes, little mechanical devices, like a small electric fan or a match box. His talk was punctuated with small quick movements of his hands and fingers, pointing for emphasis, making quotation marks in the air, and, most characteristic of all, indicating an "et cetera, et cetera," with a quick ripple-like motion of his hand. He was a short heavyset man with a large, totally bald head. He wore rimless glasses with thick lenses. He spoke deliberately with a deep Polish accent. He conveyed great understanding, warmth, and love for—but sometimes an irritable impatience with—his fellow human beings.

Korzybski insisted that most of us "copy animals" in our reactions. He believed that his new science of General Semantics would help to correct this animal-copying tendency, making us more truly human, more sane. For Korzybski, inhibition was a good word, meaning to delay our reactions, thereby promoting "thalamo-cortical" integration, using more of the whole of our brains, the newer cortical part as well as the older thalamic part.

Like F. Matthias Alexander, Korzybski insisted on the indivisibility of the self, on the necessity to practice inhibition in daily life, and on the need to live on a more conscious plane.

Korzybski had developed a neuro-muscular method of relaxing people which he called neuro-semantic relaxation. He demonstrated this on his seminar participants during an hour-long personal interview at the end of the six week seminar. Stripped to my shorts and seated on a chair facing Korzybski who was also seated on a chair, he gently took fleshy parts of my body in the palm of one hand, flexed the palm with straight fingers and then, gently pulling the flesh-muscle away from the bone, shook it gently and released his hand. This procedure he followed on all the more fleshy parts and in a different way on the face and hands. In one of his monographs Korzybski writes: "In General Semantics…we also utilize semantic relaxation which involves a relationship between 'emotion' and blood pressure, and which we have found to be very fundamental and beneficial in our work." Afterwards, when I walked down the street from the Institute to my car, I felt light, free and floating, as though I'd shed a hundred burdens.

A year later I was transferred from the V-7 to the V-12 program. I was now in uniform but continued my studies as before, at Northwestern. Sporadically I practised "neuro-semantic relaxation" on myself, but I think it tended to reinforce my tendency to collapse. I plugged away at my studies in analytical and organic chemistry and comparative anatomy, at the same time writing poetry and a few short stories. One of the latter was published in Northwestern's literary magazine, *The Purple Parrot*. This was a shot in the arm, and I was exhilarated for a few days; but like the proverbial flash in the pan, I didn't try to follow it up. In the late fall I took, with the other pre-med students, a medical aptitude test on which I scored in the nineties (as I found out after the war). Nevertheless, some weeks later, 22 other pre-med students and myself were transferred from the "medical corps" to begin training as general line officers. In January, I was assigned to the midshipman's school at Tower Hall in Chicago. After several months of concentrated study I was commissioned an Ensign. Then followed six weeks of radar school in Ft. Lauderdale, Florida. Finally, on August 4, 1944, I reported aboard the USS *Mississippi*, a World War I battleship more or less modernized. I was assigned to the Communications Division for work as the liaison officer between the radar unit of the gunnery department and the communications department.

My first night at sea was unforgettable. We were blacked out and on our way to Pearl Habor. There was no moon, and the ship was unaccompanied. I went up on deck and felt my way carefully forward until I stood near the bow. The sea was moderate, the wind blew coolish-warm and strong. I looked up and saw water stars the color of the moon, the night jewels of the sea that I had never seen nor heard of. They danced in the waves that coursed back diagonally from the prow of the ship. I stared at them disbelievingly. They seemed fateful and mysterious but also as one with the wind, myself and the huge black mass of the ship pushing steadily through the black waters of the night. Here was a mystery, some secret of life. "How can I understand this?" I wondered. Turning, I saw the great looming silhouette of the ship's foremast. The sky was luminous with a myriad of star-points and the opaque grey-black of the foremast made a space where there were no stars at all. This space or gap amidst the myriad of star-points moved slowly and regularly from port to starboard and starboard to port like the pendulum of a huge upside down clock. I gripped the handrail and looked down again at the phenomenon of the water stars the color of the moon: in them was the meaning of the ship moving through the water, the meaning of myself being there, the meaning of our purpose and destination, the meaning of the entire action of the whole world. It was all one single and simple meaning. The water stars seemed aware of this meaning.

Beneath the thick steel deck were the men, the lights and the machinery of this multi-gunned monster of war. Wrapped in the darkness of the night this mass of shaped steel seemed to have knowledge of the vulnerability of the two thousand bits of soft-warm humanity tinkering and playing with its insides. What was I, one of the bits, doing there? The ship could run itself. The men were superfluous; vanity had put them there. The thought was frightening: I felt soft, warm and infinitely crushable. But my thought shifted again to encompass the startling immensity of the starry sky and the impenetrable depths of the sea below, and immediately the great black steel shape swinging against the stars became a potent, powerful protector of myself and all my mates.

From that August night to a day in May, twenty-one months later, the ship was my home. In January 1945, we were damaged by a kamikaze attack off Luzon in the Philippines. We returned to Pearl Harbor for necessary repairs and some remodelling, mainly the covering of previously exposed five-inch anti-aircraft gun mounts. Several new officers came aboard, inexperienced and fresh from the naval academy. When we put to sea again, I found it good to be under way. As the weeks and months passed, I was convinced I could quite happily live a monkish sort of life. Except for the long stay at Pearl Harbor, I seldom went ashore when we were berthed at island bases. The thought of stepping ashore on good green or even sandy earth was unsettling.

Looking back on that life at sea, I feel a mild nostalgia for being on the sea itself, especially in the early morning—the sun rising or just up, the clouds orange and lavender tinted, as I look down from my station in radar control in the mainmast to see the great grey body of the ship ploughing through the green white-capped water and the men swabbing down the deck. The marvellous total freshness of the scene was overwhelmingly invigorating. At such times I felt there was nothing more wonderful than being right where I was.

When we were hit by the kamikaze, and the alarm sounded for general quarters, I didn't go to my battle station in the communications center several decks below, but went instead to the sick bay to see what I could do to help the wounded and dying men. I tried to comfort them and brought them water. Most were badly, some fatally, burned. When I called my department head to tell him where I was and why, he was annoyed but relieved to know I wasn't a casualty. Since most of the men and officers of the communications department had their battle station in the communications center, my presence was redundant, so I went where I could be of use. A day or so later, one of the medical officers, whom I'd watched surgically removing a shattered arm, silently expressed his appreciation.

When I was not on watch duty or asleep, I wrote long letters to family and friends, poems and short prose pieces, or I read one or another of several dozen books I had brought aboard, including works by P. D. Ouspensky[6] and Wilhelm Reich.[7] I read Proust's *Remembrance of Things Past* and found my letters home couched in proustian style. I also read a reference somewhere to the New School for Social Research in New York City whose faculty consisted largely of refugees from Nazi Germany, a "university in exile."[8] This interested me, and I resolved to investigate it after the war. My reading was turning my thoughts away from medicine to the humanities and the social sciences. My best officer friend taught me bridge, and, like everyone else in the navy it seemed, I smoked cigars as well as cigarettes. On an evening after dinner in the wardroom, sitting at the green felt-covered tables with a cup of coffee and a cigar and reading or playing bridge, I was content. Especially when the ship was under way and you were aware of the ship moving through the water because of the slow swaying and the deep-lying hum of the engines, this sense of contentment was strong. There was no nearness or a life ashore to distract. Your world was the ship, extending only as far as the bulkheads. And you were aware that throughout the ship the attention of hundreds of men was at that moment directed to the workings of this live ponderous vessel distantly throbbing and shuddering mightily with each turn of the rudder as we zigzagged across the surface of the sea. This big old first world war battleship was now come to life.

In the late spring 1945, cruising off Okinawa on pre-invasion bombardment duty we were struck once again by a kamikaze. This time the damage was light, and only one casualty, though fatal, our ship's chaplain. The plane had rammed the starboard side near the stern just missing the captains cabin. A piece of the plane's engine penetrated the skin of the ship and shot across the deck of officers' quarters like a piece of shrapnel, piercing bulkheads and finally coming to rest in the officers' mess where it injured the foot of a black mess boy who had a very bad stutter, and whom I'd been trying to help by applying my knowledge of General Semantics. The chaplain was passing the door of the captain's cabin at the moment the plane hit and was propelled violently into the passageway bulkhead crushing his skull. Making the ship's damage temporarily watertight, we pointed our bow towards a floating dry dock a few hundred miles south of Okinawa. We were convinced our next duty would be off the coast of Japan itself. But August brought Hiroshima and Nagasaki, and the end of the Pacific war. After the surrender ceremony in Tokyo Bay, we headed home for the States and the naval base at Norfolk, Virginia, by way of the Panama Canal and New Orleans where we berthed for a month and had thirty days leave.

Arriving at Norfolk in March 1946 I took a five day leave to visit the New School for Social Research in New York. I applied for admission to the Graduate Faculty of Political and Social Science, starting in September under the GI bill. In May, I was discharged from the Navy.

After a summer seeing old friends, I boarded the Pacemaker, an overnight train from Chicago to New York, a train and a ride I knew well from my two years at Hamilton. The route was through Cleveland and Buffalo, through the Mohawk Valley to Albany and then south along the Hudson to New York, the city that was now beginning to loom in my mind's eye as something huge, vaguely mysterious and unknown. As I headed into the future,

I knew there could be no turning back. And as I stared past my reflection in the window it seemed as though I alone were the reason for the train rolling swiftly across the darkened countryside, a darkness heightened by the moving points of light here and there. The long lonely wail of the train's whistle took me years back to Glencoe when, lying in bed at night, I could hear the distant bugle-like calls of the trains moving westward into the great plains.

Flying along the rails, the train gave me a kind of buoyancy as I moved in my seat or walked down the aisle. I went to the club car and, as in times past, I thought how nice it would be to meet a pretty girl and make love in her berth or mine, the inevitability of contact, our voices sounding like echoes, and knowing the loneliness of the other as we are borne swiftly across the black land. But like all the other times, I was alone with my thoughts. The decor was contemporary but seemed old and dirty. The chairs were a dark pink, the walls of the car a soiled light green with stainless steel trim. Besides myself there were three men at a table playing cards, being careful not to knock over their glasses of beer. I noted one man in particular, a heavy slouchy person with a moustache, his face jowled and marked by irregularly enlarged pores. His eyes were dull, but they glistened as if he were crying. He wore a bright colored tie pulled down from an open collar.

I took my eyes off the man. Then, a voice-like thought said to me: "You are watched. You are coming, and we wait for you. We will show you the way, and we will show you what you are. We will reveal you to yourself." These words or thoughts were sharp and distinct. Whatever it was or might be, I felt more sure of myself, my doubts bare and unsupported.

The three men had stopped playing. The fat man stretched himself, his face red and swollen. Squeezing his legs out from under the table, he got to his feet and looked at me, the only other person in the car. There was no expression in his eyes. I smiled, as if to say, "I see you have enjoyed a game of cards, but it's late and time for bed." But his face didn't change as he turned and plodded out of the car. After a few minutes, I left the club car thinking that sleep will separate two very different periods in my life.

The New School for Social Research was located at 66 West 12th Street, between 5th and 6th Avenues. Squeezed into a block of brown-stone houses, its horizontal lines and tiers of glass are in vivid contrast with the surroundings. But its brown, black and mahogany hues blend it in. I registered in the Graduate Faculty (the graduate school) and found a small furnished room a few blocks away on the corner of Charles and 4th Streets, over a Spanish restaurant. Six weeks later I found more congenial quarters in the Mark Twain house at 5th Avenue and 9th Street, sharing an apartment with a man my age who wrote comic strips. He introduced me to Morrell Gibson, a junior book editor at Doubleday and writer of children's books. She was from South Carolina and had a soft southern accent. We began seeing each other. A couple of months later I moved into her apartment on the west side of Greenwich Village, near Abdingdon Square. A year and a half later, in June of 1948, we married.

When I met Morrell she had recently ended a relationship of four years with the sculptor José de Rivera[9] and was seeing a Jungian analyst, Assia Abel, intelligent, affable, insightful, and Russian born. One night I had a rather strange and vivid dream which I related to Morrell. She described it to Dr. Abel who said it could mean I was more than ready to undergo analysis myself. I could believe it, for I was more and more frequently depressed, triggered usually by a massive self-doubt and a fear of just *being*.

The weekly sessions with Dr. Abel, which continued for three years, over-lapping my first few Alexander lessons in April of 1950 (see below), opened my eyes to the reality of my childhood and adolescent experiences, particu-larly in respect to my twin brother and my sister who had formed an alliance that grew stronger each year. An incident that stands out in my memory is the following:

About a year after our father's death, my sister, my brother and I were having supper by ourselves, mother not being home. We were sitting at the table in the dining room. The maid was in the kitchen. We started arguing and, as usual, it was them against me. Words flew back and forth, and then, seized by unbearable frustration and resentment, I ran through the pantry and into the kitchen where I grabbed the biggest knife I could find and locked myself in the bathroom next to the maid's room. There I crumpled up, crying and sobbing heavily on my arms. Some minutes later, still crying in anger and despair, I took my pencil and wrote in large letters on the wall: "I want to die and be with Daddy." Contemplating the knife in my hand, I clearly visualized plunging it deep into my chest. That seemed to be enough, for I slowly washed the tears from my face, rubbed out the message, and returned the knife to its drawer. The maid, who hadn't quite realized what I was up to, now looked at me aghast.

The more I felt like an outsider in my family, the more I swallowed my resentment and anger. Some years later when I was 14 and wearing the cast, I tried to get rid of it by belching; and that apparently, and eventually, led to the removal of my appendix. My swallowing had been so effective I was unaware of feeling any anger or resentment. I couldn't believe the psycholo-gist at Stanford who suggested my problem was my family.

December 15, 1947

Reflections and associations, for Dr. Abel: My early family experience of rejection and my own physical tendency to collapse produced a pattern of submissiveness, lack of confidence and self-doubt. I anticipated and dreaded the feeling of not being wanted. At Stanford, it was as though the school and the students were personally rejecting me. I turned the tables and rejected them. But, of course, at the same time I longed to be loved, to be part of a group, any group! But I felt I had *no right* to be part of a group. I seldom talked, even with friends or at a party, unless I had a few drinks. But I listened. When desperate to say something, to speak out, my palms sweated and my heart pounded. A massive self-doubt oppressed me at every turn. And then the depressions, the despondency, the feelings of worthlessness, of incompetence—all effort seemed futile.

In spite of the above—maybe because of it—I have a desire to be of use to people, to help people lead more productive lives. I would have been a good doctor. I seem to have too many interests. My life has been without direction, no steady goal.

July 9, 1948

More and more I see that the difficulties and problems of life are mostly obstacles of our own making. To see this is the beginning of freedom for every man. What we need is some simple teaching showing us how to live according to our inner needs. This teaching should be found in all the schools. If a man lives according to his inner needs, (though he may not immediately know what these are) he will find his outer needs, the norms and mores of his culture and society, easier to cope with. Having no fear and confident in himself, he can satisfy both.

———————•◦•———————

Pursuing my classes at the New School, I developed great interest in the sociology of language and the Sapir-Whorf hypothesis: we see the world through the lens of language.[10] But my special interest was in *conversation* as a social phenomenon worthy of analysis. I also made several good friends, including Solomon Weinstock and Ira Progoff, the latter now well-known as a depth psychologist and author.[11]

Sol Weinstock is a brilliant young fellow, only 24. We met in my class with Horace Kallen.[12] We made a joint project out of our two papers: mine on John Dewey's[13] *Freedom and Culture*,[14] his on Erich Fromm's[15] *Escape from Freedom*.[16] Every Friday night after class we met for a cup of coffee and a hamburger (he always had two), and then we would walk for a couple of hours or so around the Village talking about problems of interest. These discussions—he talked much more than I—were very stimulating. Sol was the first friend I've known in the two years I've been at the New School. But he was worth waiting for! He's about six feet, weighs maybe 230. He's never without a word—always a good one.

Ira Progoff joined Sol and me in some of those discussions after class. So also did the language scholar Allen Walker Read[17] who was then or later married to Charlotte Suchardt,[18] Alfred Korzybski's assistant for many years and after his death a leader with M. Kending[19] at the Institute for General Semantics in Lakeview, Connecticut.[20] Ira was then finishing up his doctoral dissertation, *Jung's Psychology and its Social Meaning*. Since I was in the third year of my Jungian analysis, he asked me to read and comment upon his thesis from the practical viewpoint of an analysand. This I did but do not now recall what my comments to him were. I was much impressed by his erudition, and he seemed to write as easily as he talked. Inarticulate myself, especially in earlier years, almost to the point of dumbness, I had developed a habit of observing the physical character-istics and mannerisms of persons around and with me. And I paid atten-tion less to what was said than to how it was said, the sound of the voice, the facial expression, etc. I can hear Ira speaking to me now and, interest-ingly from my later Alexandrian viewpoint, remember well his charac-teristic habit of carrying his head tilted back with a slight inclining back-wards of his whole torso.

Half-a-dozen years later, in 1954, on a visit back to the States from London, I called Ira. We met for a meal down around Washington Square. He had written several books and was especially known, I believe, for his *Intensive Journal*.[21] We talked about the Alexander Technique. He said he had read two of Alexander's books but had not had lessons. He consid-ered Alexander's work important but limited from a depth psychological and spiritual point of view. In one of his books Progoff quotes an old Hasidic proverb: "If a man has himself firmly in hand and stands solidly upon the earth, then his head reaches up to heaven." He then goes on to say:

> In this sense, man is the connecting link of the universe. In him heaven and earth come together. It is a union that is possible only because both the earthly and the spiritual are present in the nature of man. He comes from the earth, but he stands upright. And this sym-bolic aspect of his physical structure, his posture with respect to the cosmos, reveals the elusive two-fold quality of human existence that must always be remembered in the study of man.

I like the "posture" of that passage. It puts in stark relief the poignancy of man's deteriorating posture.

As the weekly sessions with Dr. Abel continued, I was slowly freeing myself from what seemed like years of bondage, though within the limits of an essentially unchanging manner of using myself. It seemed a struggle without end, as the following 1949 entry from my journal may attest:

February 17, 1949

I am everlastingly concerned with the question, "What am I good for?" At the age of 28! I have a mania for self-doubt! Which may be my undoing if I cannot put an end to it. So easily am I depressed. My work bogs down because I have a chronic doubting disease. Such anxiety! My God, it angers me to think of it. The world is a sad and miserable place. Yes, this is what my anxiety does for me. Life is worthless, or living? To hell with "life"! Let's talk about *living*! Get it on an active plane.

I always seek encouragement, praise, some sign of appreciation or respect, no matter how slight. So childish. All is so personal with me. Nothing exists on a disinterested or business-like level for me. I feel caught in the trials and insecurities of social life, social distinctions and so on. These things never meant anything to me in the past. Maybe that's my trouble. Most of the time I feel ignorant of any reality but my own measly feelings and sensations. Inverted, that's me. Twisted inside out, like an orange peel.

I have a new tic on my left nostril. First conscious of it when Morrell's friend Lois came over for tea. I was waxing the floors downstairs when I sat down and felt the tic for first time. This makes two, counting the old one over my left eyebrow. Someday I'll be a mass of tics, that or an alcoholic.

Christ! What a creature. You crawling, snivelling, God-forsaken idiot. Full of nameless fears, a product of years of frustration, submission, passivity—a classic neurotic! Of all of this I was unaware, until recently. Now all I can feel is resentment, anger. Should I let it all go at once? I check myself. I try to behave rationally, to be civil. It's the old story, I don't want to hurt anybody's feelings.

February 20, 1949

I read in *The New York Times Review of Books* about the letters of Sherwood Anderson. Anderson said writing helped him to reach people. Writing turned his attention from himself to others. Preoccupation with the self makes you a mess, he said. He wrote letters the first thing every day, as a preparation for his story writing. Perhaps writing would be good for me, if it would help to externalize my feelings. It would certainly help me as a would-be sociologist. It would help the same way painting does. When I was painting last summer,

I became more aware of things, more perceptive of shapes and colors. It made me realize how little we actually look at things around us.

———————◆———————

Towards the end of my third year of graduate work, I had begun working on the outline for my doctoral dissertation, *Conversation and Sociability*. In this project, I was being greatly encouraged by my thesis adviser, Professor Alfred Schütz.[22] But I was bothered by the feeling of being about as far away from real life as one could get. Nothing but books, piles of them, on the floor, on my desk, and endless taking of notes. I wondered if I was going about this research business in the right way. I had bought a large filing cabinet and was slowly, over the months, filling it with my notes. It might look thorough and efficient to an outsider, but I wondered just how much I was really getting out of it. It took so much time and energy, I thought there must be a better way. I wanted to be creative in this business. Dry-as-dust scholarship wasn't for me. I knew that. But here I was plodding away day after day, night after night, reading and taking notes. I became a hermit in my room, which didn't contribute much of anything positive to our marriage.

I worked all day and no sooner was dinner over than I went upstairs to my study. I would have liked to stay down and be with Morrell for a while, but when I did, I felt guilty at not getting on with my thesis, which wasn't going well. Sometimes it seemed as if I were marking time, playing with life, getting nowhere, taking notes to no purpose. How utterly inadequate I could feel! What misery I felt! This can't go on indefinitely, I said to myself. I've got to get my thesis done, get my degree, and get a job. The money won't last a lot longer. So far I had been lucky a few times in the stock-market, just enough to keep my capital more or less stable. But it was capital we were now living on. The awful thing was this: though I clearly saw the three steps I must take—thesis, degree, and job—I felt I would never make them. I could not see myself making them. "How stupid, silly and ridiculous," I told myself. "Why must I feel this way?"

After we had married in June of 1948 we had rented a cottage for the summer in back of a large house in Ridgefield, Connecticut, belonging to two elderly ladies who were ardent Jungians. Morrell knew Ridgefield because Jimmy Wyckoff, a writer and friend of the sculptor José de Rivera (Morrell's ex-boy friend, as I said earlier) lived there with wife, Lois, and little boy, Angus. We saw them just about every day and became close friends.

Ridgefield was a stately New England town. Magnificent elm trees and mansion-sized estates lined Main Street. Most of the stores and businesses were also on Main Street. Towards the north end stood two large homes facing each other from opposite sides of the street. The house on the west side belonged to the mother of a family I would get to know extremely well a decade hence, following my return from London as a qualified teacher of the Alexander Technique. The house on the other side, named Casagmo, belonged to Miss Mary Olcott who, starting in 1920, became a pupil, friend, and then benefactor of F. M. Alexander. I found this out when, in 1961, I read her obituary in the Ridgefield Press. Miss Olcott was 97 when she died. I interrupt my narrative to quote two paragraphs from her long obituary, followed by a letter from Miss Olcott to the Department of State, Washington, DC.*

>...Miss Olcott later became interested in the teachings and writings of F. Matthias Alexander of London. She not only helped Mr. Alexander establish his training school in London, where a new technique in education was taught, but she even undertook the revision of the proofs of two of his books: *Constructive Conscious Control of the Individual* and *The Use of the Self.*
>
>In 1940 when London was bombed Miss Olcott was among those who enabled Mr. Alexander to establish his school in the United States. She sponsored four of the children he brought from England as pupils of his school in Stow.
>
>*The Ridgefield Press*

Department of State, July 10, 1941
Washington, DC.

Dear Sirs:

In regard to Mr. F. M. Alexander and his school at Stow, Massachusetts, it gives me much pleasure to say that I have known Mr. Alexander since 1920 both in England and here and that I can gladly vouch for him in both countries. As one of his pupils I know and can vouch for his work and himself. His books are the most completely scientific in the line of

---

* This and other letters between Miss Olcott and F. M. Alexander in my possession I owe to the kindness and generosity of Miss Olcott's niece, Countess Bianca Bertocci-Fontana, of Assisi, Italy.

education, and the most honest that I know. His scientific attainments are beyond question and his school here, like his school in England before the war, reflects his breadth of vision and his knowledge in the highest degree.

I consider that it is an honor for the United States to have Mr. Alexander, his teachers and his school here.

> Yours very sincerely,
> (signed)
> Mary Olcott

When the summer ended and it was time to move back to our apartment in the city, we were more than reluctant to leave the country and the fresh air to say nothing of our friends the Wyckoffs. Then Lois told us she had seen a house for sale in South Salem, a village just five hilly miles from Ridgefield, driving along West Mountain Road. We drove over to have a look, and that was enough. Taking a ten thousand dollar 30-year mortgage, I paid the selling price of $20,500.

It was a seven room house—originally a farm house built in 1872—white clapboard with blue-green shutters, set on five acres, the back three all woods. Two huge elm trees towered over the front of the house and one even larger in the back on slightly sloping ground towards a red barn with white trim. To the left or north side of the house, flush against a long rock wall, stood two giant maple trees nearly as tall as the elms in front.

South Salem was in the north-eastern corner of Westchester County in New York state. Three days a week I took the train from Katonah (a seven mile drive from our house) to Grand Central station in the city and then a 5th Avenue bus or a Lexington Avenue subway to my classes at the New School. Beginning my third year of graduate school, I asked for and received permission to skip the Master's degree and go directly for the Ph.D. Our house was exactly 50 miles by car on the Saw Mill River Parkway to the middle of Manhattan.

My sister, Anne, was married to the commercial artist, Paul Rand,[23] and they lived in Rye, New York, about 20 miles from us. There were weekly visits between our households. Two or three times a week we saw the Wyckoffs. And there were half-a-dozen friends from the city who visited us on occasional weekends. The social life counterbalanced my long hours of study and work on my thesis, and also Morrell's cogitations over her writing. But I was exasperatingly uncertain about leading an academic life. And I was oppressively preoccupied with mostly negative feelings concerning self. And Morrell herself, bright, articulate, and with a kind of innocent childlike charm, increasingly showed me another aspect—her face changing as though coming from bright sunlight into a dimly lit room, the skin drawn taut and mask-like. Assia Abel explained this to me as her "negative animus." For Morrell at these times I was "soft" and "half-a-man." Our love life was increasingly marked with long dry spells, punctuated by thirst-quenching oases.

In the fall of 1949, Morrell took a part-time job at a book shop in Ridgefield specializing in used books. And one day that fall as we walked along Main Street under the arching elm trees, Morrell turned to me and said I was "lurching from one side to the other" as I walked. A few days later she came home and handed me three books she thought might be of benefit for me to read. I decided to read only one of the books, *The Universal Constant in Living*, by F. Matthias Alexander. I chose to read it because of the title and because of the introductory essay by George E. Coghill.[24] I remembered seeing Coghill's name on a list of scientists and others who Korzybski believed to be moving in "new" non-Aristotelian directions. And I was struck by Coghill's opening paragraph:

> The practice of Mr. F. Matthias Alexander in treating the human body is founded, as I understand it, on three well-established biological principles: (1) that of the integration of the whole organism in the performance of particular functions; (2) that of proprioceptive sensitivity as a factor in determining posture; (3) that of the primary importance of posture in determining muscular action. These principles I have established through forty years in anatomical and physiological study of Amblystoma [a species of salamander] in embryonic and larval stages and they appear to hold for other vertebrates as well.

Reading Alexander's book I came across such sentences as "our manner of use is a constant influence for good or ill upon our general functioning"; and "there was evidence of over-action of muscle groups due to misuse, the influence of which had been constantly operating against any form of treatment." This was a language that struck a strong cord in me, though I do not actually recall thinking of my years of back trouble nor even considering this book could be a help to me in this respect. What I remember most vividly is the impression I had that the author was writing with conviction and confidence about something—our "manner of use"—basic and important in our daily living. I absorbed every word of the book and knew, without knowing just why, that its message was important for me.

Finishing the book, I sent a letter of inquiry to the publishers, E. P. Dutton. Their reply stated they could not give out information on their authors. However, they gave me the address of the Alexander Foundation School in Media, Pennsylvania. Without delay I called the school and spoke to Mrs. Philomene Barr.[25] She said she and her husband drove to New York City each weekend and gave their lessons at a hotel. I made an appointment for the following Saturday.

Arriving on the appointed day, Mrs. Barr explained that her husband was assisting her, though he was not himself as yet a certified teacher. I was standing in front of a chair, Mrs. Barr on my left, Mr. Barr on my right. Let me say again that my more or less total state, bodily speaking, was one of *collapse*. Bearing this in mind, the reader may appreciate my surprise at finding myself rising or lengthening up out of my pelvis at the touch of their hands. I had the sensation of being propelled upwards and outwards by some force being released within me. This initial experience was for me, as it has been and is for Alexander pupils the world over, a total revelation. The following week, Morrell joined me in the weekly lessons, and later, so did the Wyckoffs.

My first lesson was in March and they continued until late in June—the year was 1950—when the Barrs left for their summer teaching in Santa Barbara, California. We resumed our lessons in the fall. In January the Barrs announced to me that they had acquired enough additional pupils in the Ridgefield, Connecticut, area to make it possible for them to teach there rather than New York City. So I invited them to give their lessons in our home, which they did.

Some weeks later I had one of those super experiences that many Alexander pupils have at some point in their re-education, though, of course, for a variety of different reasons. Like most teachers, the Barrs first did chair work, then table work. On this particular occasion they were concluding the lesson—they got me up off the table and sent me on a walk across the room. And right then, as I walked, I felt my back supporting me, lifting me, as never before in my life. I felt my spine as a sturdy column of dynamic support. The sensation was so utterly new and overwhelming that I began laughing and weeping simultaneously as I tried to describe to them what I was experiencing. But my words were unnecessary—they had grins on their faces from ear to ear.

May 4, 1950
I got a lot of good study done yesterday, about ten hours. I feel so much better doing good concentrated work. There is also work to be done outside and inside the house, social visits, and so on. I need to apportion my time better.

I'm learning that to do good work you have to make the work a habit and also to saturate yourself in it so that you live what you are doing. It's a kind of self-stimulation, breaking down resistances, and carving out new or deeper channels for the energy to flow more easily and directly.

I'm reading *The James Family*, by F. O. Matthiessen.[26] He killed himself several weeks ago because, according to a note he left, he found the present state of the world impossible to live in. Henry James, senior, has excellent things to say.[27] His ideas on God, man and nature could be given an interesting Jungian interpretation. I think I feel deeply about "religion" but wonder if I overtly neglect it because of intellectual and *milieu* reasons. Interest in religion seems to be growing in America, perhaps due to the war and the prospect of another more terrible one. If we could see how irrational we are underneath our pseudo-rationality, our daily pretence to explicit knowledge of "cause and effect;" and if we could really know we are simple creatures with marvellous potentialities yet to be realized—perhaps then we and people everywhere would more readily accept our condition, our common humanity, our common ground, and give up our old impeding habits and beliefs. Sapir says the study of other peoples' languages has a liberating effect. It reveals *our* unique view of things; people with a different language see the world differently.

May 7, 1950

We went to Anne and Paul for dinner last night. The rabbi Joachim Prinz[28] and his wife were there. When I mentioned my thesis subject, "Conversation and Sociability," Dr. Prinz was immediately interested and encouraging. He grasped the problem and made suggestions. For the first time I felt neither tedious nor embarrassed to talk about my thesis.

I must schedule my time better and stick to it. On Saturdays we go to the city for our Alexander lessons; Sundays we usually see Anne and Paul. Mondays I'm in the city for classes. This leaves only four weekdays for work on term papers and my dissertation.

I think how far removed my work is from the dangerous state of the world—Britain's Bevin thinks Russia will go to war by 1952![29] I ought to do something that has at least some bearing on the world situation. The least and maybe the best I can do is to do my daily work and hope to contribute to the happiness of my friends and family. But, remember in your teens how you used to feel about such things? You believed that if you could raise your voice the world would hear it and end man's unhappiness and war between men. The enthusiasms and dreams of youth are wonderful. If we could hold on to them in spirit it might be a force to do good work now. And I begin to see that speaking in a circle of friends, in conversation, is no different from speaking to a far wider circle encompassing the earth. In both circles, the responsibility is there, and it is the same.

May 16, 1950
I want to be a more natural person. I want to say what I think without fear of being hurt. I rationalize this fear into a fear of hurting others when all along I'm afraid of hurting myself. Well, that's the pattern I've woven for myself. Maybe now I can unweave some of the threads and let the whole pattern fall apart.

You will not hide! Why be afraid to show yourself to your fellow-man? He is like you in all basic respects. And like you, he is afraid and doesn't want to be. Express yourself and pursue your aims, neither fearing rebuttal nor failure. Your relationships will be transformed. You will have new respect and love for yourself that leads, as Erich Fromm says, to more real and bountiful love for others.

May 23, 1950
I took Alfred Schütz's exam yesterday in the sociology of language and believe I did well. Now to keep the schedule of work preparing for the exam. Much will be accomplished. I notice I'm beginning to think of myself as a sociologist. This is new—taking myself seriously, in a definite role. And I don't see it as limiting; but rather, expanding. To grow in this life, roots are needed, an anchor thrown out, a foundation built. I'm accepting myself as a teacher and looking forward to it.

May 28, 1950
Had an excellent Alexander lesson Saturday. I'm getting the "feel" of the thing. As John Dewey said about this work, the meanings keep opening up as you go along. But I must do more "thinking"—each act, every day, stop and think!

June 1, 1950
Stayed up all night working on the outline of my dissertation. Went in to town early next morning with a friend who spent the night with us and finished outline at her apartment just a few minutes before appointment with Dr. Arvid Brodersen, my second thesis adviser.[30] He liked it, congratulated me, and even said he was "excited" by it. How confident I feel now, with the outline done and well received.

Reading Holbrook Jackson's *The 1890s* with great interest. Many books on the "art of conversation" were written in that decade, frequently described as decadent, though Jackson convincingly points out that there were as many elements of regeneration as degeneration.[31] It emphasized "correctness," the "right way to live." Conversation was regarded as a "lost art," and not a few social observers and writers were intent, in one way or another, upon reviving it. A few good conversationists were still around, like Oscar Wilde[32] and Aubrey Beardsley.[33]

There may well be a connection between interest in conversation as an art and "decadence." Jackson lists perversity, egoism and artificiality as characteristics of the decade. When conversation is cultivated for its own sake, perhaps *that* is artificiality. But what about sociability? Certainly, egoism has no place in good sociable conversation, at least not the strident variety. Simmel, the great German sociologist, writes about the "artificial world of sociability" and its "superficial" character.[34] I would say yes and no to this. Is it true that men in their *natural* state, as Hobbes thought, are always at war?[35] When men are together out of "pure" sociability, if not of love for one another, are they being unnatural?

July 9, 1950
A letter from Professor Carl Mayer[36] (my third thesis adviser) this morning. He has no objections to the outline. He thinks the subject needs study and that what I say will be interesting, though it may not be convincing to him.

June 15, 1950
My life is so full and interesting now. I always knew that if I could work consistently and creatively, life would be a joy! I'm reading Guglielmo Ferrero, a man of much penetration, many insights.[37] When you visit friends, work in the garden, or just enjoy the sights and sounds of summer, you can do it wholeheartedly, because you know you are getting on with your crucial work. If you are not then the pressure and the anxiety color every word to a friend and every act addressed to the soil.

July 16, 1950
Had a real good talk with Dr. Schütz on Tuesday. He advised me to keep a "scientific diary" in addition to my journal, a practice of his for years and of great benefit.

August 28, 1950
Résumé of summer: we spent a delightful week in Canada, visiting our friends and their four children. And with the help of Paul and other friends, I finished the porch which wraps around the south-east corner of the house starting from the front door. Needs one more coat of paint.

Have an idea for a book, or anthology: selections from fiction writers illustrating sociological ideas, terms, categories, etc. This would aid the sociologist in giving a little concreteness to the abstract. For example, Nathanael West's chapter on the crowd or riot in his *The Day of the Locust*.[38] Literature, of course, is a reflection of social life; but it also illuminates it—like a mirror reflects light on a dark area. I would also like to collect writings on the regeneration and transformation of the individual and society.

October 23, 1950
Today I am 30 years old! For most of those years I've been relatively free to think and do whatever was my desire, urge, inclination, ambition. Be thankful for that and remember it during hours of despair and depression and faced with tasks demanding all the will and intelligence you possess.

Looking back, I see countless hours wasted, energy dissipated, projects not finished, studies not completed, lessons thrown away—so much come to nothing because of fear and doubt. So many hours dreaming! Another thing was my abject ignorance of the culture and world I live in. My world was one of such utter subjectivity I could not really judge or measure anything. Even now I am not much beyond that perspective. Some people bind and gag themselves worse than others!

The truth is I am now preoccupied with my development as a human being. I evolve still, and I want to continue to do until the day I cease all operations. Personal satisfaction and self-respect will not be my lot until I can plan a piece of work and *know* that I will carry it out. Is this what having faith in oneself means? Some of this faith must come from experiencing the fruitfulness of one's efforts. Tomorrow begins a new decade. Ten years from tonight I pray I shall look back with more to be thankful for and less to regret.

During the winter of 1950-51, after five or six months of Alexander lessons, I was beginning to realize myself confidently and productively. When I read over the entries in my journal (which I did not do until the mid-l960s), it was easy enough to see the transition from a man with doubt and anxiety and the "faint heart," as I called it, to a man with confidence and willingness to accept responsibilities.

However, my life with Morrell, while improved in some respects, was slowly deteriorating in another. More or less subconsciously, I was becoming aware of a growing attachment between her and Jimmy Wyckoff. Jimmy was now living full-time in New York City while his wife and son continued to live in their house in Ridgefield. He told Lois he couldn't survive as a writer living with her and Angus deep in the country, 55 miles from the excitement and stimulus of the city. So he moved to an apartment in Greenwich Village. In February or March of 1951, Morrell began making weekly visits to the city, spending the day and sometimes staying overnight with her girl friends. I knew she had to see her ex-colleagues at Doubleday about some stories she was working on for a children's book. Almost twice a week, Jimmy wrote long letters to us on yellow legal-pad paper, describing his experiences and his feelings and anguish as he struggled to bring the novel he was working on to completion. Morrell read these letters aloud to me. I enjoyed the letters, was really interested in what he had to say, and felt a little proud that he found in my wife such a sympathetic "sounding board." ·

April 9, 1951

I will do good things in the world. I will realize the capacities within me. I feel no anxiety in saying this, and *that* is a sign of my new attitude towards self and the world. Attend to what must be done today, tomorrow and the next day! Don't go beyond this. Study, reflect and act, and all will be well. Expect frustration and despair, but use their energy for further work. Know, finally, and be secure in the knowledge, that you are a sociologist. *Be* a sociologist, then. Sociology is your mainstream, and you can nourish *that* with your painting, your writing and your music. The job to be done now is to finish the thesis. Say what you have to say, and be done with it. And stop worrying about the impression it will make on your professors—a worse example of *end-gaining* (Alexander's term) can hardly be found.

Fear nothing, and, above all, don't fear yourself! Live and love! Write letters and extend yourself. *Expansion* is the great thing, not contraction. Start work on an article for a journal. To write is to express and expand. It is a flowing of inner energy to the outer world where others can read and share your experiences. Always there are others, though it may seem at times there are no others learning and appreciating. So, you energize society, including people you know and love, live and work with. The experience of every individual can be fuel to society. Others may look to you for life and energy. Society feeds on you. This is a responsibility. They have faith in your honesty and openness. In giving you receive. Look at Boswell's *London Journal* 1762-1763 as an example of what I'm saying.[39] His journal is a fascinating document that has inspired me to write more often in these pages. Boswell's day comes to life for us in our day. Who can say that Boswell, or even his time, is dead? For three days Boswell has been living a life within me. Isn't this immortality? Transform your energies to outer forms, in writing, painting or music; and love and be loved. *There* is your immortality.

If there is a *first* law of society, it must be this: You are because of others. So act, speak, write, and live with and for others. Perhaps there is a "primary control" in society analogous to Alexander's primary control in the individual. Just as some disease and disability in the individual is a consequence of ignorance and interference with the primary control, so social conflict and war may be a consequence of ignorance and interference with the necessary and natural reciprocity of all of man's social relations.

April 13, 1951
The Barrs have arrived to give their lessons. From now on they will spend the night with us on their visits from Philadelphia to give lessons in the New York-Connecticut area. They need to carry their lessons over through Saturday morning. Norris Barr said my mother had arrived and was staying at the Hotel Media. I hope she takes her lessons regularly.

April 22, 1951
This journal will be a record of my trials, failures and successes during this fourth decade of my life. With growing awareness and conscious control, it will be a decade of accomplishment.

I begin to live in the way I've always known I could live with a strong faith in myself. Only recently have I begun to acquire such faith. I used to think my dreams were illusions. I know now they are not. Ordinarily we give only lip-service to the old adage, "Know thyself!"[40] We need to experience its truth in ourselves.

April 27, 1951
This week has been a bad one. I must recover and work hard. The Barrs are downstairs giving their lessons. I want to live and be more active, be more of a husband and a lover to Morrell. I am still the cautious creature. I want to take chances with people and with life itself. What it comes down to, I suppose, is I wish to take chances with *myself*. I have nothing to fear, nothing to hide. I must live and not be afraid. Yesterday, I hated the city and myself because I was afraid, afraid that the posters I was doing for the New School were no good and that I was simply foolish for volunteering to do something I wasn't capable of doing. I felt incompetent in *all* respects, and I was afraid I'd sit in a bar and drink myself into a stupor. I looked at the people in the streets, all kinds of people, and I wondered how they could bear the city and their own loneliness and obscurity.

What am I? I am everything and nothing; part sociologist, part businessman, part artist, part writer, part husband, part child, part man; parts of all of these, not wholly any one of them. This could be my strength. So far, I think, it has been weakness rather than strength. Even this is hard to judge. As a boy, I recall how I said that before I die I want to see every land, every country, every people, including the North and South poles. Similarly, I wanted to experience everything experienceable, to be everything, to be all things to all men. The strange thing is, perhaps it is a terrible thing, I feel I *could be anything*. I have felt myself embrace the world, holding everyone in my arms; loving all and being loved by all.

Other times I am afraid to love anyone, even those closest to me, or to *be* anything at all. So, what am I? Am I mad, or just an average middle-class neurotic? Am I the little boy who wants all the candy in the store? Recall my boyhood friendships: I wanted to be the "best friend" of each one of my friends.

I had a brief talk with Constance (Jimmy's sister-in-law) after her lesson with the Barrs. She talked and I listened. She said she was terribly depressed and had been for almost two months. I knew she had been feeling depressed but it's deeper than I thought. She wanted to go off and be alone with herself and would have done if the children hadn't been there to keep her. She said she had been just "poisonous" to her husband but he was bearing it nobly. She felt life wasn't worth living. Why do anything? What's the good of it all? In the evenings, she couldn't talk to her husband, just ran upstairs to bed. As she went on, tears came to her eyes. She said that was happening often lately, she just felt like crying. She asked me if I had felt like this "yet." I said I was all too familiar with depressed states, but it was reassuring to know how others experienced it. She thinks this may be going on with Jimmy. As for me, I don't know whether my sharp depression of the last few days is a result of my lessons or not. I feel like saying "Who knows? Who knows anything?"

It's now 11.30 p.m. Had picked up Morrell at the train, drove home, and had dinner. Then the Barrs returned from their dinner, and we had a pleasant evening's conversation. In consequence, I feel much better in every way. They are rejuvenating people. I want to devote more time and energy to the Alexander work, spend more time thinking about it, to stop and inhibit. Mr. Barr said tonight, "Without inhibition, man has no choice."

April 28, 1951
A few months ago I enrolled in a Saturday morning painting class at the Silvermine Guild in New Canaan, Connecticut. We paint in oils, from the live model, sometimes dressed, sometimes nude. Today we had a nude model, and I made quick sketches of a variety of poses. My drawing became freer and freer and, at the same time, more controlled. I drew with vigor and enthusiasm, moving around, doing "whispered ahs," remembering the guiding orders and wishing my arm and my whole self to be light, free and alive. Later I did some reading and writing and thought about Chapter III of my thesis.

Jimmy came out last night to gather more of his belongings. He's found a room on 11th Street, between 5th and 6th Avenues. He returned to the city this afternoon. Lois was upset and said she hopes he doesn't come out again. Well, this must indeed be the end of their marriage. I saw him briefly. We seemed to have little to say to each other, which isn't the case with Morrell and him. Over the past four months they've established a very sympathetic relationship. I know he suffers over his writing, and living apart from Lois and his son must be unsettling to him, and I understand that he finds it easier to talk to Morrell about his problems than to me. But I find myself resenting it. Sometimes I feel like an incidental third party when the three of us are together. Perhaps I shall have much more to say about all this later.

Peter (Jimmy's brother) had dinner with us. He was very funny. I laughed for the first time in a long while—a good hearty laugh, I mean.

April 29, 1951
It is hard to write now, but I feel I must do so. Morrell told me today that she wants to leave me—not a divorce, necessarily, but a separation, for a time, at least. She feels we are not good for each other. I have felt this too, but today the thought of life without her is almost unbearable. Just last January I proposed that we separate for a time. Now I can't believe I ever said it. I'm trying to fight the terrible feeling of emptiness. Everything now seems pointless, without any meaning at all, I must succeed in conquering it. I know she is determined to go. How much do I blame myself! I feel that I do not understand anything, least of all myself.

April 30, 1951
"Thank God for a beautiful day," I said to myself when I woke up this morning. I found the sun shining, the sky all blue and the fresh clear green of the new spring here and there on the trees and on the fields and shrubs. If it had been hot and cloudy and oppressively humid like yesterday, it would have been awful.

I must decide what I'm going to do, stay here or live in the city, until we come together again, if ever. If I stay out here, the Barrs can continue giving their lessons here. But where will I be able to work better? I must finish my thesis!

Afternoon. Mrs. Brook is here cleaning the house. I have put up the screens on the windows. Morrell and I lay in the sun for half an hour and had a pleasant and friendly talk. I feel much better, look forward to my work, am ready to plunge ahead. Morrell hasn't decided where she is going—South Carolina (her home) or Virginia Beach or with Lois to a beach on the Sound. Then to the city to do some work in publishing and her own writing.

I have decided to remain here, in South Salem. Morrell thinks I'll be too isolated. But I will work hard and try to keep decent hours. I'll do some work on the cracked plaster walls in the rooms upstairs and fix the barn up to use as a studio for painting.

Last week I read over some old letters and was impressed by the encouragement I've always had from friends who have known me well, who have known I would do good things in the world if only I can keep control of myself, overcome apathy and depression. The letters reveal a basic confidence in me. Morrell has always expressed similar sentiments to me, especially recently. She thinks I can be a "great man" in my own way, but I must fight for it. Sometimes I feel like I'm balanced on a knife edge—on one side the blackness of doom, despair and deterioration; on the other, the light of a productive and useful life! But when I feel most lonely, restless and depressed, I can know and realize that behind me, reinforcing my own desires and struggle, is the faith of those friends. I will incorporate their faith in my own faith in myself. Remember: "No man is an island!"[41] As for practical working tools, remember: no end-gaining! Think of the means-whereby. Do some work every day. Devote your attention to the immediate problem.

I painted for about an hour this afternoon but ended in depression. Morrell returned from town and I revived. We had an Old Fashioned,[42] and I was in fairly good spirits during dinner.

Evening. I feel again sad and depressed. I should work but it seems like a dismal task. Morrell is in bed. I must not allow myself to be swallowed up in a quagmire of self-deprecation and despair. It is strange, but since yesterday my head has felt very heavy; it feels like wanting to fall back all the time. The back of my neck is even a little sore. This is a warning to me: I must not forget my *guiding orders*. I must stop and think before every activity.

May 2, 1951

Morrell has left for about a week. She will be back next week. Before she left I asked her if she were in love or seeing someone else. She said no but she knew a lot of men and would see other men. I said I expected this since we're separating. She said I wanted to know if there were another man because I wanted to feel "rejected." I denied this. Actually I felt I'd rather have her leave me for someone else than for some such reason that I'm a failure, bound to be unsuccessful, or generally inadequate. I didn't say this to her. But I think there is someone else and I would like to know who it is. Last night she said she didn't want to tell me everything now, that what she had said was enough.

May 9, 1951

I'm in Media, near Philadelphia, where the Barrs live and have their school, the Alexander Foundation School. I drove here today. It is now midnight. I've heard nothing from Morrell, but since last Thursday night, have come to the shocking realization that Morrell and Jimmy went away together. I called him last week after Morrell left and I was in the city. I hoped to see him and thereby relieve some of the misery I felt over her departure. But he wasn't home. His landlord told me he had gone away for the weekend. I had the feeling he was telling me something I already knew.

May 10, 1951
I got up at 6:45 and I've had breakfast. At 9:30 I see the Barrs. The Hotel Media is small, a converted old house, cheerful, clean and friendly. I'm thinking of coming back in a week's time and stay for the three weeks the Barrs have before leaving for their summer teaching in Santa Barbara. Mother is here, too. She will drive back with me to New York and take a train home to Chicago. She is anxious to get home.

6 p.m. Just finished my best lesson with the Barrs. Norris said I had my best lengthening. "When you have that, you have a gold mine." I really feel I came away with something. Today was a big jump!

In the morning I was at the Alexander Foundation School, met the teachers and some of the children. It was wonderful. Very cheerful, gay and relaxed. The children were so absorbed in their work. I watched Mrs. Barr give the children their three minute lessons as they sat in the class room. I learned much from observing their freedom and flexibility and ease of manner.

At eleven o'clock I went to see Norris at their home. We walked about outside talking about the Alexander work and other things of interest. I was completely at ease. I asked why they didn't seek an endowment for their school. He said even if they were anxious to have an endowment it would not be easy to get one. People who endow, he said, prefer "men in white coats, peering through microscopes." He said they were content to get along as best they can, preferring a "few dozen" people who are really interested and who will carry on and spread the work. He said an interesting thing: "Perhaps there is a basic law in nature, of which Alexander's principle is only a special case."

After lunch, mother and I went to an auction on the Samuel A. Biddle estate. We bought nothing, but I sketched several of the watchers. First time I've sketched in public. Too self-conscious to do it before. Haven't told her about Morrell and I separating. I said Morrell was in South Carolina visiting her family.

9:30 p.m. Mother and I are back in the hotel. We had dinner in the nearby town of Westchester. The thing between Morrell and me seems like a dream. But I must confess I thought it would happen or had to happen, sooner or later. But it is sad. I feel sadness in thinking of it, in realizing that our lives, from now on, will be unknown to each other.

May 18, 1951

Anne and Paul are going to Europe for two months, sailing June 29, and they have asked me to go with them. I've decided this would be a good thing for me to do under the circumstances. And I will meet F. Matthias Alexander. I will rent the house for the summer season, at least. My thesis will suffer, but in the end it may profit from such a journey.

The Barrs are coming today to give their last lessons of the spring. They will resume again in the fall, though I shall probably be living in New York City then. I don't know. I may, in fact, live in London and study the Alexander Technique, doing my other work also, of course. I would like, I think, eventually to teach the Technique. What could be more useful? I really feel I would make a good teacher of the work. The "talents" I have all seem to converge on it.

May 19, 1951

Had a long conversation with the Barrs last night. Mrs. Barr went to bed around eleven, Norris and I an hour later. We discussed the work. Barr: "We've only about half-a-dozen pupils who really see the possibilities of Alexander's work, which are limitless. I sometimes wonder about the fruitfulness of our attempts to teach the heathen. In 500 years there may be about 100 persons who really understand and carry out the work in their lives." G.B: "That seems a very small estimate. 500 years is a long time." Barr: "The work is not easy. It's the most difficult thing there is. Americans, especially, will find it difficult because their whole way of life tries to find easy ways of doing things, shortcuts. They want everything easy and cheap. They want to be 'cured' of something and we don't cure, as you know. They want to be able to walk out 'cured' after four or five lessons, or rather 'treatments,' not lessons, is what they want."

May 26, 1951

I was in the city yesterday to get my passport and to book a passage on the *Ile de France*, sailing June 29. Thursday evening I had dinner with Georgie Robert at Ricky's. She separated from her husband, Jean, a Swiss businessman from Geneva, a year and a half ago. They were both good friends of ours. Georgie is a writer, and her first novel will be published this fall. The six of us, including Lois and Jimmy, were all good friends and now we are all separated. That very evening I had dinner with Georgie, Jean was having dinner with Lois and, of course, Jimmy and Morrell were together. In June,

Georgie goes to the MacDowell Colony in Vermont and I will rent her apartment while she's away.

June 2, 1951

Went to bed at 12:30 and woke up at 3:00. Set free a moth trapped in heat register. Didn't feel like sleeping, so got up to write in my journal which I've been neglecting recently. As I lay in bed I realized I was beginning to feel a power in myself, a certainty of accomplishment. I no longer thrash blindly about in the underbrush but walk forward easily and confidently. The feeling is no doubt partly inspired by this morning's conference with Arvid Brodersen. He said he had only words of encouragement about my thesis (I had given him the first 90 pages to read), and he thinks I am making an "original contribution" to sociology. We talked about Europe and meeting in Paris sometime in August. He has a "brilliant" friend, Alexander von Schelting, who will be there then and would like me to meet him. He said von Schelting would be much interested in my thesis, and the three of us should have good talks over it. I recalled reading von Schelting's critique of Karl Mannheim's "sociology of knowledge." Brodersen said von Schelting was a charming, somewhat over-refined, aristocratic person, talented artistically and a fine pianist. He left Germany when Hitler rose to power, went to America and then to Switzerland, where he was when war came in 1939.[43]

June 22, 1951

Morrell called yesterday evening to find out how the house was coming (preparing it for renting), what day I leave for England, etc. After hanging up, I was struck with a feeling of intense sadness. But this soon passed. A little later I picked Lois up and went to The Hayloft for dinner.

I've been working steadily on the house for the past three weeks, painted the woodwork in the dining room, the upstairs bathroom and the porch floors. I love to paint and have gotten pretty good at it. I repaired the floor in the hallway and remodelled the bookcase in the big bedroom. Doing this bit of carpentry, I've noticed how more efficiently I work than a year ago when I built the bookcases for the bookshop in Ridgefield. I attribute this to my Alexander lessons. I found, as I worked, that before I would make a move, I rehearsed each step in my mind, which, of course, is being aware of the means-whereby.

Have just been walking around the house. It is a beautiful spring morning. The trees and bushes are full and green. A rose bush is in bloom. The shrubs I pruned so radically two years ago are now spreading full and green.

The raspberry plants look wonderful. It will be a good crop which I won't be here to enjoy, but my tenants will.

June 23, 1951
I have been so busy but feeling so wonderful in spite of what has happened with Morrell and me. I am beginning a new life. I feel new forces in myself— as if unleashed. For the first time in my life I feel like *acting* in the world. I'm getting impatient with discussion and analysis, impatient with words—I want only to *allow and do*.

Part II

My Lessons with
F. Matthias Alexander

1951 — 1953

J uly 4, 1951

After a stimulating and restful six-day voyage on the Atlantic, we disembarked at Plymouth, England. We had Paul's small van on the boat with us, and so, after loading our baggage and ourselves into it, we set out for a friend's house in Byfleet, Surrey, about 30 miles south-west of London. We arrived at 2:00 in the morning.

July 11, 1951

My first meeting with F. M. Alexander, at 16 Ashley Place, about a five-minute walk from London's Victoria Station. I was admitted by the secretary, John Skinner,[44] who sat down with me in the waiting room. We talked about Alexander's work and the training course. I learned that there are ten students in the teachers' training course who worked every day, except weekends, for three hours per day, that the minimum period of study for a teacher's certificate is three years, and that Alexander had tried working with pupils as a group but had found this unsatisfactory. Other than Alexander, there are about a half-a-dozen teachers in London. After about twenty minutes, Mr. Skinner showed me into Alexander's teaching room, the room where, as I already knew, Alexander had been teaching for forty years.

The feeling I had from the moment I entered the room—and this feeling was to grow during the lesson—was one of timelessness; that is to say, of time as we usually think of it having no importance.

The room looked to me as I thought it must have looked in 1910, when Alexander acquired these rooms and taught his first pupil in it. The woodwork was dark-stained, the walls beige-colored, liberally hung with pictures, including a large portrait in oils of Alexander, and a series of antique china plates grouped around the mantelpiece. On a wide and deep sofa against the wall by the door was an enormous round pillow covered in black silk. In the far corner near the windows facing the street was a desk stacked with books. On the mantelpiece, judiciously placed, were numerous *objets d'art*. Against the wall to the right as one entered the room, and behind Alexander's Queen Anne teaching-chair which faced the front windows, stood a stately grandfather's clock that sedately tick-tocked away the seconds. Whether or not it was true, I felt that nothing had been significantly changed in this room from the day Alexander taught his first pupil in it, to the moment of my standing there.

Beyond all this the feeling of timelessness was due to the character of the man who now entered the room and whom I liked on the instant. His eighty-three years showed in his white hair and lined face, but those years were belied by the warmth, intelligence and vitality that emanated from him. His figure was slim and erect, and his hair beautifully white and abundant. He greeted me warmly and began the lesson.

The lesson was the third thing that gave me the sense of timelessness: the sense, paradoxically, of time passing and having passed, yet, at the same time, the sense of something permanent, constant and inviolate throughout this passage; for I had the knowledge that this aged, creative and fully alive man was teaching me, in this Victorian room, a principle of growth and change biologically rooted in man as an organism.

I thought at that moment of my own country with its ceaseless quest for novelty, for any kind of change so long as what is brought forth is new, a quest so compulsive and pervasive that family life was becoming fraught with restlessness, dissatisfactions and anxieties.

But here now was a man who had discovered a primary principle of change and growth in man as a species, and who had devised a technique for teaching this principle to others. He was clearly not interested in effecting or seeking changes in the ordinary accoutrements of living which are, on the face of it, so important to the satisfactions of most other men.

And if civilization, or civilized life as we have come to know it, is rushing headlong to a violent end, could this be partly or indirectly attributed to the fact that man has all but lost the art of growth and change within himself—which depends, as Alexander's work has so clearly demonstrated, on the development of man's inhibitory powers—and that he is now almost universally ignorant of his power to reclaim it?

I was with him this first visit for little more than a quarter of an hour. He talked little while using his hands on me, asking a few questions now and then. The touch of his hands was something I'll always remember, gentle, with now and again light, gradual pressure. Standing at my left, he put his left hand on top of my head while his right hand explored my back. I felt as though he sensed my entire being. It made me glow!

July 16, 1951

Occasionally I have to remind myself that I am in England. Of course, all that one sees is a reminder, but you can look about and forget your strangeness; feeling quite as if you have lived all your life here. I do feel "at home" in England, so much so that it makes me wonder if I should have always lived here. When I think back to just a month, even less than a month ago, and South Salem, New York, I am amazed at the transition, the sudden and complete change from one life to another: I know I am on the threshold of a new and wonderful life. But I have a touch of anxiety, the anxiety one experiences when confronted with the unknown.

This week I will see Alexander on Wednesday, taking Anne and Paul with me.

July 18, 1951
After lunch, Anne, Paul and I went to see Alexander. I for my second lesson, they for their first. Afterwards, they said they felt weightless and floating— they were amazed.

———•———

I saw Alexander once more before leaving in early August with Anne and Paul to travel by car in France, Italy and Switzerland. I returned to London in early September.

September 7, 1951
On August 30, I said good-bye to Anne and Paul in Paris. They drove to Le Havre and set sail for America the next day. I returned to London yesterday with no hotel reservations and everything booked up. But Hotel Bookings, Ltd. got me a "service flat" in Cork Street, in the heart of the West End.

I went to see Alexander today with the intention of finding out if I could join the teachers' training course. After some discussion, we agreed that in view of the uncertainties about my time over here and about my own life plans, I should continue with the private lessons. We had a good talk, and among other things he said the following:

"The best thing to do is to wait until you can make a decision and then stick to it. You know, teaching this work is a wonderful career, a wonderful career, but very difficult. The training course is three years, but it ought to be six years. This is so true that sometimes I've felt like giving up the course altogether."

"Of all my pupils, including John Dewey, [Aldous] Huxley, the Archbishop of Canterbury,[45] [Sir Stafford] Cripps,[46] Bernard Shaw,[47] no one of all my pupils was ever able to keep to the decision to not do what they felt was the right thing to do. That's the trouble."

> For the trouble is that when reason is so far held in check that it
> loses its power of denial, it must have lost its power of control.
>
> (MSI, p. *102*)

"People always try to do the right thing, whereas they should concentrate on not doing the wrong thing. They have an idea of what is right, but because of the sensory appreciation they have or bring with them, their idea of the right is wrong."

…in any attempt to make necessary changes in himself, man would need to do what *feels wrong* in order to *be right*.

(MSI, p. vii)

"I tell a pupil to 'sit down,' but then I say, 'Don't give consent.' You see, I have to give the stimulus to do the wrong thing, otherwise there is no opportunity for him to say 'no' to doing the wrong thing, to say: 'No, I will not sit down!' Isn't that true? And yet it nearly always happens that when I tell a pupil to 'sit down but do not give consent,' he will still try to sit down. That's the trouble."

"If I had the time, I could write half-a-dozen books on just this one thing, 'sitting down'- for everything is all there in the simple act of 'sitting down.'"

"We want to change. But how are we going to change if we go about doing things the way we have always done them? Yet, people are never able to grasp this idea. And after all these years I know why this is so: none of our education has ever directed us to do differently."

…*a human being functions as a whole* and can only be fundamentally changed *as a whole*.

(MSI, p. vi)

"You know, I've so often found that even the most diploma'd men are the stupidest. A friend of mine wanted me to meet one of the most educated, one of the most diploma'd men alive. I met the man, a doctor, and I never met a more stupid man. I said to my friend, 'What did you want me to meet that damn fool for? I'm a fool and I know it, but he's a damn fool and doesn't know it.'"

"But my work has penetrated, there's no doubt about it. Twenty or thirty years ago, I was condemned for using the terms 'psycho-physical,' 'means vs. ends,' 'means whereby,' and so on, but today they are commonplace."

…I have persistently avoided using words which are labels for ideas and "systems" which I am convinced are fundamentally unsound,… If the reader will remember that the subject of my study has been, and is, the living psycho-physical organism, which is the sum of a complex of unified processes, he will understand why I refrain as far as is possible from using such terms as "postures," "mental states," "psychological complexes," "body mechanics," "subconscious," or any of the thousand and one labelled concepts which have, like barnacles, become attached to the complicated idea we have of ourselves owing to the kind of education to which we have been subjected. Instead I prefer to call the psycho-physical organism simply "the self," and to write of it as something "in use," which "functions" and which "reacts." My conception of the human organism or of the self is thus very simple, but can be made difficult by needless complication resulting from the preconceived ideas which readers bring to it.

(UCL, pp. xxxii-xxxiii)

"Don't think that I don't appreciate your coming to me. I do. I always appreciate it when young men and women come to me. I don't understand it sometimes, but they do come. For I know what you went through before you came to me: nothing you ever learned or experienced, nothing that was ever taught you, prepared you to come to me, did it? [No!] There, you see, but yet you came."

"Well now, you come to me as you've decided—you are staying here for three months at least, you've made that decision—and you will be able to see better what the difficulties are. Then you can decide what you want to do; and we will do it. Whatever you decide you want me to do, I will do it."

"Your great compatriot, Dewey, once asked me at a dinner we attended together what I would regard as the best test of a person. I replied, 'A person who can make a decision not to do a certain thing and then stick to that decision.'"

September 8, 1951
Today the thought came to me that I might learn to inhibit negative or unconstructive thoughts and feelings about myself in the same way that I am learning to inhibit the impulse to stand up or to sit down—simply by saying No! If negative thoughts and feelings don't produce constructive self-criticism or creative work, they waste energy, are self-defeating and end in depression. The Alexander Technique provides the means to redirect the energy.

Every living human being is a psycho-physical unity equipped with marvellous mechanisms, and it is through these when set in motion by the stimulus of some desire or need that all reactions take place. Every reaction, therefore, is associated with a particular manner of use of these mechanisms and, because of the closeness of the association, it is this manner of use that constantly influences all manifestations of human activity, whether labelled manual or mental.

(UCL, p. 3)

September 11, 1951

Alexander talked considerably, and I had, I thought, a good lesson. At its conclusion he seemed pleased, and we said good-bye till Thursday.

He began the lesson by remarking on the weather, what a good day this was for a change. He said he had reports from friends in many places of erratic weather; and of all the places he had been, London really had the nicest weather when it was good, especially in the spring. Then he turned to matters concerned with the lesson.

"To change one's habits, that's the hardest thing of all. And in all the years I've been teaching, no one, not excepting the great people I've had as pupils, including the two in your country, Dewey and Coghill, was able to keep to the decision *not* to 'sit down' after I told him not to give consent to the order to 'sit down.' In the beginning that is—afterwards, they learned it."

> Habit, indeed, may be defined as the manifestation of a constant.
>
> (UCL, p. 6)

> ...I use the word "habit" in its widest sense, as the embodiment of all instinctive and other human reactions which observation shows to be determined by the manner of use of the self as a constant influence operating for or against us under given circumstances and at a given time.
>
> (UCL, p. 80)

"In all our activities, we tend to pull our heads back and contract or shorten ourselves. We give ourselves an order or direction to do a certain thing, and then we fight against ourselves in doing it. Whereas the head naturally wants to go forward and up and the back to lengthen and widen. That's all there is to it. But it works. Whatever we may think about it, there it is!"

"You allow the head to go forward and up and the back to lengthen and widen. When the back widens, this takes the pressure of the ribs off the lungs, thus allowing breathing to become naturally deeper, allowing the ribs to expand and contract, giving freedom to the floating ribs. My technique, because of its effect on breathing, has stopped cases of angina. What happens when people suddenly suffer pain? They contract, pulling themselves down and inwards—[Alexander demonstrated this contraction by pulling his arms close to his body and hunching over]—whereas, if they would undo themselves, they would be all right. It's the undoing that is so important. I once had an epileptic pupil, and during a fit he pulled his head back so far that it touched between his shoulder blades."

"In the middle of your chest, there's a bone, the sternum, and the upper ribs are attached to it. Farther down, the ribs remain unattached. Put your hands on me, and you will feel the floating ribs."

Mr. Alexander turned his back to me and directed me to place my hands just above his waist. At first I pressed a little, as if I should try to probe or feel for his ribs. But he said, "Don't press, just let me place your hands." He did so, and then I observed a most remarkable movement in his breathing. Alexander is of slight build and, therefore, one ordinarily would not expect to find such a capacity for expansion and contraction in rib movement. Nevertheless, here was this movement, all so free, easy and regular. He called my attention to the fact that I could hear no sucking or gasping of his breath. I was frankly amazed, and I said to him that I had no idea such movement in breathing was possible, a movement that was confined, it seemed, almost entirely to his back. He replied: "You have a wonderful frame and soon will have a beautiful movement down here," and he placed his hands in the region of the floating ribs.

"'That which we would not do, we do; that which we should do, we do not.'[48] Do you know that? It is in the Bible, and when I read it, I thought it was such a pathetic confession. I don't often read the Bible, because there is so much in it I can't agree with. But that sentence is so pathetic a confession, don't you agree?"

"We talk about the subconscious. Well, this is one way of looking at this work: we are raising the subconscious to consciousness, so that we govern ourselves by consciousness alone."

September 13, 1951
A good lesson. Mr. Alexander asked me to tell him why I wished to go into the teachers' training course. I told him I was deeply interested in the work and I believed, as a result of my experience so far, that teaching the Technique would be a profoundly interesting, useful and satisfying career. The upshot of our talk at today's lesson was that Alexander suggested I enter the training course on a provisional basis for one year, but that we postpone a final decision until the next lesson the following week. He said that it was obvious to him that I was very interested in the work and that he never wanted to make the mistake of discouraging young people having such interest.

September 17, 1951

Mr. Alexander said he thought it might be unwise for me to join the teachers' training course because of the current troubled and uncertain conditions on the international scene. It might be difficult to maintain the school and there was even the possibility of my having to return to America prematurely. Under these circumstances, he said, it would be better to continue with our private lessons. I was sorely disappointed but nevertheless decided to do as he suggested.

———————•———————

My "disappointment" didn't last too long, because I soon realized, had I at this time entered the training course, I would very likely have forfeited these lessons with F. M. Alexander.

September 19, 1951

A very good lesson. Alexander talked quite a lot, and he appeared to be in more than his usually good humor. He joked about matters ordinarily calling for sober reflection, and mimicked the speech of the Irishman Cheiro, the famous palmist.[49] He looked most elegant in a dark blue, double-breasted suit and bow tie. His eyes are brilliantly blue, his face sensitive and finely lined. His head, neck and back all seem to be linked up together as one harmonious unit. He talked about his meeting with Cheiro and how the latter had prophesied the purchase of 16 Ashley Place, Alexander's teaching quarters. Alexander said there was much in this matter of reading the hands—"No doubt," he said, "that hands show history." About the so-called extrasensory capacities: "Persons who have this can't explain it, or tell how they do what they do. We can't explain any of these things from our present subconscious way of doing things. But we'll be able to explain a lot of these things from the more conscious level of action."

> …at some period of his evolutionary progress the human creature must have reached a psychological moment to pass from the subconscious to the conscious plane of control.
>
> The change from a subconscious to a conscious plane of control would have involved a knowledge on man's part of the *means whereby* he would be able to command a conscious, reasoning direction and control of his psycho-physical mechanisms in all activity.
>
> (CCCI, p. 5)

He joked about some men repairing the street in front of the house: "It's an awful business—they don't do anything, you know. What's going to happen when people in countries like Japan get back to rebuilding their civilizations, while we over here have forgotten how to work?"

"We want to get rid of the idea that we can't go ahead and do a thing. When we do something well one day, but fail the next—that's an awful business. We don't want that, do we?"

"Life is the developing of conscious control and confidence."

> Confidence is born of success, not of failure, and our processes in education and in the general art of living must be based upon principles which will enable us to make certain of the satisfactory *means whereby* an end may be secured, and thus to command a large percentage of those satisfactory experiences which develop confidence, as against a small percentage of those unsatisfactory experiences which tend to undermine our confidence and make us unhappy.
>
> (CCCI, p. *185*)

> Health in living…may be defined as the best possible reaction of the organism to the stimuli of living as manifested in its use and functioning. To ensure this we require as a *constant* the best possible manner of use and the highest possible standard of functioning at a given time, in a given environment, and under given circumstances; and this I submit constitutes the ideal of human attainment in the field in which we are interested.
>
> (UCL, p. 68)

September 20, 1951
Excellent lesson. Alexander seemed pleased.

He said little and then only of things concerned with the lesson. I was again impressed how in sitting down or standing up we thwart our intentions. When rising from a chair we tend to pull the head backwards while thrusting the torso forwards, thus doubling or tripling the energy needed to get up from the chair. In sitting down in a chair, instead of simply allowing the knees to go forward, we duck the head down or pull it back on to the neck while sort of hunching the torso forward and stiffening the legs and then falling backwards into the chair. When we perform such acts not once but many times in a day, the cost to the organism must be considerable.

> The word *co-ordination* is ordinarily used at the present time in as narrow and limited a sense as the words relaxation, readjustment, re-education, etc.
>
> I use the word *co-ordination*, both in its conception and in its appli-

cation, to convey the idea of co-ordination *on a general and not a specific basis*. Specific co-ordination of any specific part of the organism, such as the muscles of the arm or leg, may be brought about by means of a direct process, during which process, however, new defects in the use of the organism in general will certainly be cultivated, whilst others already present will become more pronounced. These harmful conditions will not be cultivated if the specific co-ordination is brought about by means of an indirect process involving, primarily, the general co-ordination of the psycho-physical organism—that is to say, an integrated condition in which all the factors continue to make for satisfactory psycho-mechanical use.

Co-ordinated use of the organism means that there is satisfactory control of a complex mechanism.

(CCCI, pp. 8-9)

September 24, 1951
Best lesson so far! Alexander said: "You're doing beautifully!" And I knew I was. I couldn't help but smile during much of the lesson. After a particularly good moment, he walked a few steps away, as he always does when he has something special to say, and said: "There, you have it! Now that you have it, you can't make a mistake."

October 1, 1951
Alexander said very little this lesson, one which proved difficult for me. I came away impressed once more, and increasingly so, by the great obstacles that habit places in your path when this path is a new one. The difficulty I experienced during this lesson seems to contradict the awareness I had of much progress the preceding week. Actually, there is no contradiction. Because each lesson brings something new. You see something you didn't see before and really couldn't see, simply because you did not and could not know it was there to be seen. But this is not quite right either, for the "something" that you can now see this week simply was not there to be seen last week.

The following passage from John Dewey's introduction to Alexander's *The Use of the Self* is very much to the point of the above entry:

The vitality of a scientific discovery is revealed and tested in its power to project and direct new further operations which not only harmonize with prior results, but which lead on to new observed materials, suggesting in turn further experimentally controlled acts, and so on in a continued series of new developments. Speaking as a pupil, it was because of this fact as demonstrated in personal experience that I first became convinced of the scientific quality of Mr. Alexander's work. Each lesson was a laboratory experimental demonstration. Statements made in advance of consequences to follow and the means by which they would be reached were met with implicit scepticism—a fact which is practically inevitable, since, as Mr. Alexander points out, one uses the very conditions that need re-education as one's standard of judgment. Each lesson carries the process somewhat farther and confirms in the most intimate and convincing fashion the claims that are made. *As one goes on, new areas are opened, new possibilities are seen and then realized; one finds himself continually growing, and realizes that there is an endless process of growth initiated.*

(UoS, p. xix, my italics)

October 3, 1951
Alexander talked a lot today.

"A compatriot of yours has just left. She's come over here to take lessons. There are three of you Americans here now, but before the war we used to have as many as sixteen here at one time. Oh yes, oh yes."

"Why, when I taught in New York, I worked all day long, from eight in the morning to eight at night. From about 1914 to 1924, my brother and I alternated, six months in London, then six months in New York."

"A time came in my work when I knew I had something that shouldn't be lost, and I needed support in order to go ahead with my teaching. So I went to New York, on the Lusitania, the first ship to go through the submarine patrols. On my arrival, I gave a few speeches to some important people, and the result was that the way was cleared for me to go ahead. A friend suggested I set up headquarters in the Essex Hotel. I went there and got a suite of three rooms, a beautiful hotel. I asked the price, and they told me it would be $ 3,000 for four months. Oh, my dear boy, what was I to do? I had no idea it would be that. I thought it over, and then I proposed an agreement on the results of the first two weeks of my teaching. They accepted, and the results were so good, I could go ahead."

Because of the war, Alexander received his Government's permission to evacuate the children of his school to America. The school took children of ages three to eight and was established in 1924 at Alexander's teaching quarters in London. Some years later, however, the school was moved to

Bexley, Kent, where Alexander had purchased a home. Much to Alexander's regret, it was not feasible to re-establish the school after the war. However, its sojourn in America was sufficient to give birth to a similar school in the United States under the supervision of A. R. Alexander.[50]

———————•◦•———————

"In 1941, the Whitney Homestead at Stow, Massachusetts, was turned over to us rent-free to set up our school for children. Oh, it was a beautiful place, a large house with much acreage."

"When I went to New York [during World War II] I found everything changed. None of the people I had known in the old days [1914-1924] were there any more. All those people of so much fine taste were gone. London is changed, too. It isn't like it used to be in the wonderful days from 1904 to 1914."

"Oh my, I've had all the advantages of life. My father's and grandfather's estate was passed on to us… Then coming to London in the beautiful period from 1904 to 1914. … And then, too, knowing the good people in New York during the years I taught there."

"Once I was at a party in New York, and we had to open seven bottles of fine old wine before we found one that hadn't been spoiled from being kept in an over-heated cellar. Wine and cigars need a constant natural temperature. I have a room here, situated in the middle of all this string of houses, that never varies in temperature, winter or summer, and I keep my cigars there. The cellar, too, is the same way."

"The hardest thing in the world for us is to keep to a decision. That's why I put a chapter on it in my last book. John Dewey once asked me at a dinner we attended together, what would be my test of a person. Well, I said, a man who can decide what the thing is he should do and then sticks to his decision to do that and not some other thing. You see, we decide to do a thing, and then we find out the means whereby that thing can be done."

"Oh, Dewey was a bad pupil, as he'll tell you himself. He had many lessons. But it saved him. He's an old boy of 89 or 90 now. When first he came to me, in 1914 or '15, he was like this—[Alexander stooped over and shook his hands nervously]."

———————•◦•———————

In the above entry, Alexander clearly implies that Dewey's lessons in the Technique enabled him to live his long and productive life. From all accounts, it seems that Dewey himself agreed with this. The following passage is from Max Eastman's *Heroes I Have Known* (1942).[51] The reference to Alexander as a "physician" is, of course, wrong:

…[Dewey] had recourse to a very unconventional physician named Matthias Alexander, who opened a new chapter in his life. Dr. Alexander is an Australian of original but uncultivated mind [sic], attacked by the medical profession, but possessed in Dewey's opinion of a valid theory about posture and muscular control, and a technique of "re-education" by which human beings are supposed to recover that integration of the organism which is natural to animals. Dr. Alexander has been endorsed by others as brainy as Bernard Shaw and Aldous Huxley, and his system undoubtedly worked in Dewey's case. "I used to shuffle and sag," he says. "Now, I hold myself up." Every one of his friends will endorse that assertation. And when he adds that "a person gets old because he bends over," it is difficult to argue with him, for he is obviously an expert on not getting old. It is simply impossible to believe when you see him that he has been around since 1859! Dewey gives 90 per cent of the credit for this to Dr. Alexander, 10 per cent to a regular physician who taught him to keep things moving through the alimentary canal.

"My boy, as I've told you before, you have such a beautiful back, I wish I had it, and it's a great shame if you don't use it. Once you get that widening of your back, you will be all set. And you get it by allowing the head to go forward and up, by freeing the neck…"

October 8, 1951
A very good lesson. I think I made a big jump ahead today. After a question from me, Alexander told me about the large muscles of the back that "never tire," what some physiologists call the "anti-gravity" muscles.

Alexander said that it was only after ten years of intensive self-observation, working with mirrors, that he discovered what he called the primary control, the "mechanism" that governs the distribution of muscle tonus to the trunk and limbs, influencing, directly or indirectly, the working of the body musculature. When our manner of use is such that we interfere with the primary control, so then do we restrict ourselves, in one way or another, in performing an act or movement.

Perhaps the best description of the primary control to be found in Alexander's books is the following from *The Universal Constant in Living*, pp. 6-7:

> …I discovered that a certain use of the head in relation to the neck, and of the head and neck in relation to the torso and the other parts of the organism, if consciously and continuously employed, en-

sures, as was shown in my own case, the establishment of a manner of use of the self *as a whole* which provides the best conditions for raising the standard of the functioning of the various mechanisms, organs, and systems. I found that in practice this use of the parts, beginning with the use of the head in relation to the neck, constituted a primary control of the mechanism *as a whole*, involving control *in process* right through the organism, and that when I interfered with the employment of the primary control of my manner of use, this was always associated with a lowering of the standard of my general functioning.

October 10, 1951
A good lesson. At one point I felt my lower back shift backwards without any "doing" on my part. I mentioned it to Alexander, and he said: "That's where it belongs."

At one point during the lesson, Alexander said:

"You're not thinking connectedly."

"The less you do, the better off you will be."

"Why, your back has terrific power. You could lift twenty times your own weight with it. It's a crime if you don't use it."

"In 20 or 30 years, people are going to be madly trying to take lessons in my technique. I won't see it, but you will. And why? Because by that time people will realize that something has to be done."

> The blind continue to lead the blind in the twentieth century as in the days of the cave-man, but the process brings with it more disastrous results in our time than was possible in those early days of man's more limited spheres of psycho-physical activities.
>
> (CCCI, p. *176*)

October 17, 1951
I have been very discouraged the past week, which included two lessons for which I have made no entry. I see now that, in spite of myself, I am still *trying to do, trying to feel*, etc.

During today's lesson, Alexander certainly noted the difficulty I was having. He stopped his teaching, stepped a few paces away, and said:

"You know, if one ever expects to teach this work, one must above all, first and foremost, have acquired a fully adequate standard of conscious control in the use of himself. For without this, a teacher cannot convey at all or in any way hope to give to the pupil the experiences necessary for learning the Technique. Why, if you should watch some of the teachers in the training course, you would see exactly what I mean. I walked in one day, and one of them called to me for assistance, saying he could do nothing with the particular student he was working on. I didn't look at the latter at all, only at this would-be teacher, and said, 'No wonder, look at what you're doing with *yourself* in the process of trying to teach him!'"

"Another young man who has had almost two years in the course, came to me today, and I said to him: 'My dear fellow, you will never be able to teach this work, since you have never yet succeeded in abandoning the idea of trying to sit down, of trying to stand up, and so forth.'"

All of the above paragraphs are concerned, in one way or another, with what Alexander calls *end-gaining*.

> According to...the end-gaining conception, all that is necessary when an end is desired is to proceed to employ the different parts of the organism in the manner which our feeling dictates as necessary for the carrying out of the movements required for gaining the end, irrespective of any harmful effects due to misuse of the self during the process...
>
> It will be seen therefore that end-gaining involves the conception and procedure of going *direct for an end* without consideration as to whether the "means-whereby" to be employed are the best for the purpose, or as to whether there should be substituted for these, new and improved "means whereby" which, in their employment, would necessarily involve change in the manner of use of the self.
>
> (*UCL*, p. 10)

"Why, Mr. Binkley, when I am teaching you, as I do now, I am able to convey to you what I want to convey, because as I touch you, and guide you with my hands in carrying out my instructions, I, myself, am going up! up! up!"

October 25, 1951
At the end of this lesson, Alexander said to me: "Don't imagine you have had a bad or a disappointing lesson. For we had a good lesson, the way a lesson should be. It's the way I would like to have all my lessons, if my pupils would only let me!"

It had happened twice during this lesson that, when Alexander was ready to take me out of the chair to a standing position, I simply could not be moved but was like a rock. For I had decided that if I could not follow

Alexander's instructions I was simply going to do absolutely nothing at all, that I was going to resist with all my might the temptation to push myself up with my legs. It was only later that I realised that this firm refusal on my part to do anything at all actually involved a decision to do something, i.e. to resist, rather than a decision to allow.

> In my experience, as soon as the pupil is asked not to do anything, he will immediately show all those signs of strain and fixity of attention that he shows when he is asked to do something, and which we have learned to associate with any attempt at concentration. Point this out to the pupil, and he will answer, nine times out of ten, "I am trying to do nothing!" He actually believes that he has something *to do* to do nothing. To such a point can we be led by our belief in concentration!
>
> (CCCI, p. 164)

> When it is explained to…a pupil that inhibition is the first step in his re-education, that his apprehensive fear that he may be doing wrong and his intense desire to do right are the secrets of his failure, he will invariably endeavour to prevent himself from doing anything, by exerting force usually in the opposite direction.
>
> (MSI, p. 154)

So, while, at the time, I had felt stupid and chagrined at my apparent failure to follow Alexander's instructions, I left Ashley Place feeling very good about his parting words. I suspected that the struggle I was having would be, in the end, at least my particular key to learning the Technique and making its principle a permanent acquisition.

And, today, I saw myself nude in a full-length mirror for the first time since beginning lessons with Alexander. And I was almost startled to observe a flexibility in my torso, in expansion and contraction during breathing, that was completely new to my eyes.

> …a gradual improvement will be brought about in the pupil's sensory appreciation, so that he will become more and more aware of faults in his habitual manner of using himself; correspondingly, as with this increasing awareness the manner of his use of himself improves, his sensory appreciation will further improve, and in time constitute a standard *within the self* by means of which he will become increasingly aware both of faults and of improvement, not only in the

manner of his use, but also in the standard of his functioning generally.

(*UoS*, p. 43)

For instance, with the improvement in his use he will become aware of an increase in the expansion and contraction of the thorax—i.e., of the degree of thoracic mobility. Reliability of the sensory register is essential to all who would make permanent changes from unsatisfactory to satisfactory conditions of functioning.

(*Ibid.*)

November 2, 1951
Alexander said to me today: "As I've told you so often, you have such a powerful back that when you do misuse yourself, you do it twice as badly as the next fellow!"

During the lesson I had fallen over backwards and grabbed hold of Alexander's arm with one hand and the back of the chair with the other in order to keep from falling altogether on the floor.

Lately I have felt a very severe strain or pull on the top of my thighs while sitting in the chair during the lessons. On these occasions it has been a positive relief to me when Alexander has taken me to a more forward position on the chair. I mentioned this to him. He immediately placed his hands on my thighs and said: "But, you see, there is no tension there. Feel them yourself." I did so and could feel that the muscles were indeed free from undue tension, not tightened up as they had felt. He said I was experiencing a "new pull," that where I felt strain, there was no strain. And so this was only another indication of the unreliability of my feelings or sensory appreciation. He said you must test with your hands in order to determine what is actually the case, since we cannot rely on the sensory feeling.

In answer to a question I put to him about breathing, he said: "Don't say to yourself, 'Now I am going to breathe!' Pay no attention to it. Only, free your neck, allow the head to go forward and up—this brings about a contraction of the ribs, forcing the breath outwards, and then, at a certain point, air will, at its own pressure, enter to fill the lungs, expanding the rib-cage, widening the back."

I think it is important for me, for anyone who wants to understand this work, to realize that the neck being free, the head going forward and up, the back lengthening and widening, the ribs contracting and expanding, etc.— that these activities are parts of one continuous connected event or process.

It is also important not to rely on feeling as a guide in freeing the neck and directing the head forward and up, etc. As Alexander continually points out, reliance on feeling results in trying to *make* the head go forward and up, rather than *allowing* it to do so. With the energy of the *directing* process, the head will go forward and up when the neck is free—when one stops pulling the head back and down or forward and down and when one stops tensing the neck. It is a question of thinking the matter out, of determining just what it is we are doing that interferes with the *primary control* and to stop the interference.

In *Constructive Conscious Control of the Individual*, p. 88, Alexander writes: "...volition is used to name *what we intend to do*, and inhibition to name *what we refuse to do*..." But there is no hard and fast line separating the two. The inhibitory phase of the act may overlap and carry into and through the volitionary phase. One comes to understand this in practice, that is, during lessons.

> ...in the application of my technique the process of inhibition— that is, *the act of refusing to respond* to the primary desire to gain an "end"—*becomes the act of responding* (volitionary act) to the conscious reasoned desire to employ the *means whereby* that "end" may be gained.
>
> (CCCI, p. *118*)

> [Inhibition] involves a form of non-doing which must not be confused with passivity...
>
> (UCL, p. *107*)52

> The primary procedure in the technique...is the inhibition...of our habitual reflex activity. To succeed in this means education in the fundamental sense, for it calls for a conscious recognition and understanding of all that is concerned with the formation of habit, and of the means whereby habits can be changed.
>
> By this initial inhibition change becomes possible...
>
> In this whole procedure we see the new principle at work, for if we project those messages which hold in check the familiar habitual reaction, and at the same time project the new messages which give free rein to the motor impulses associated with nervous and muscular energy along unfamiliar lines of communication, we shall be doing what Dewey calls "thinking in activity." As far as we can judge, mankind has not had the experience of thinking in activity where the projection of messages necessary to the employment of the primary control of his use is concerned. In the ordinary way man has just reacted instinctively to any stimulus to activity, whereas in the new plan which I am

suggesting the messages, preventative and otherwise, must be consciously projected *in their right sequence* throughout the activity.

(UCL, pp. 91-92)

November 7, 1951
Last night I was reading *The Use of the Self*. I read the preface and Dewey's introduction slowly and carefully. Then, not intending to read more as I had some other work to do, I turned to a few pages at random and read there. But then, though I had already read this book once, I became so absorbed in Alexander's account of his experimental work with the aid of mirrors in investigating the use of himself, that I continued to read further. I found myself utterly struck with the idea that Alexander was here trying to get across to his readers, namely, the unreliability of our feelings, of our sensory impression and appreciations. I thought I had already understood this idea, but now, it seemed, I was really grasping and understanding it for the first time.

I lay down on the divan, wanting to think the matter out, to digest carefully this idea I had just swallowed, tasting it fully for the first time. What came to me then, suddenly, was a wonderful sense of being free, of having just been cut loose from something hampering, restricting and burdening. What came to me next was the realization that this sense or experience of freedom is the inevitable consequence of being able to reject feelings or sensory appreciation as unreliable; you could no longer be a slave to them. Being unreliable, they can only mislead, taking you where you don't want to go, not taking you where you want to go, giving you false information about yourself, other persons, the world around you.

I realized that once you refuse to accept your feelings at their face-value, the consequence is, as surely as night follows day, a general *un-doing* of yourself, which is another way of looking at the word "freedom." It must be, indeed, that most of us, most of the time, are dragging ourselves down, burdening ourselves all unknowingly by habitually trying to feel our way, trying to sense our way through life and being hopelessly misled in the process.

The alternative to helpless reliance on our feelings and "instincts" for guidance in behavior is reliance on *conscious* direction and control of use. Failing this alternative, we can scarcely avoid putting undue stress on our sensory mechanisms, imposing such a burden on these that some sort of "breakdown" becomes all but inevitable for so many of us. The "nervous breakdown" may well be a sign of sensory mechanisms strained to the point where even a minimum degree of clarity and order in their functioning is no longer feasible under the old conditions.

This unreliability of our sensory appreciation suggests certain ideas and practices in other fields. In the physical sciences, for example, we have learned not to rely on unaided sensory impressions or observations. We have, instead, developed many kinds of instruments, measuring devices and objective tests in order to construct more accurate statements about objects and events in the world around us. In courts of law it is well known how various may be the interpretations of witnesses to the same accident or event. In the psychiatric and social sciences the degree to which persons often misunderstand or misinterpret the behavior of others is an issue of primary concern. Far from seeing people as they are, we see them as we *make* them to be, thus adding our bit to the "thousand natural shocks that flesh is heir to."53 Misinterpretations and misunderstanding seem to be more characteristic than not of our social relations. In the more serious instances of these, psychiatry tells us that the misjudgments may result from something faulty or pathological in the self, that the center to which we refer the impressions we get in our interpersonal relations is not functioning aright, being, perhaps, too heavily freighted with childhood traumas and consequent inflated/deflated self-images, etc.

But now, for over fifty years, Alexander has been saying and *demonstrating* that our feelings (sensory appreciation) are unreliable, why they are unreliable, and what can be done about it. In *The Use of the Self*, p. 16, he writes, "I had proved in my own case and in that of others that instinctive control and direction of use had become so unsatisfactory, and the associated feeling so untrustworthy as a guide that it could lead us to do the very opposite of what we wished to do or thought we were doing." If this is so (and the experiences I've had so far in my lessons have shown me beyond any doubt that it is so), is it not reasonable to suppose that this unreliability or untrustworthiness of feeling as a guide in what we do may be an important factor in misinterpreting the acts and words of others, in misjudging our own motives so far as we make any attempt to understand them and, in fact, in preparing the way for so much of the "mental" illness that, notwithstanding Freud and Jung et al., puzzles us all?

When our sensory appreciation is deceptive, as is the case more or less with everyone to-day, the impressions we get through it are deceptive also. The extent of this deception depends largely upon the extent to which our manner of use has been put wrong and the nature and degree of the faulty guidance of deceptive feeling. When a certain degree of misuse has been reached, the deceptiveness of these impressions reaches a point where they can mislead us into believing that WE

ARE DOING SOMETHING WITH SOME PART OF OURSELVES WHEN ACTU-
ALLY WE CAN BE PROVED TO BE DOING SOMETHING QUITE DIFFERENT.
This is equally true of things we believe we think, which more often
than not are things we feel.

(UCL, pp. 24-25)

Sensory appreciation, from our point of view, has a much wider
significance than is generally attributed to it. But it will be sufficient
at this point to state that, taken even in the most limited sense, it
includes all sensory experiences which are conveyed through the channels of sight, hearing, touch, feeling, equilibrium, movement, etc.,
and which are responsible for psycho-physical action and reaction
throughout the organism.

If we raise an arm, move a leg, or if we make any other movements
of the body or limbs, we are guided chiefly by our sensory appreciation
or, as most people would put it, by our sense of feeling. This applies to
the testing of the texture of a piece of cloth between one's fingers, or
the gauging of size, weight, distance, etc.—in fact, to the employment
of the "physical" mechanisms in the processes of hearing, seeing, walking, talking, and in all the other activities of life.

(CCCI, p. 21)

November 11, 1951

I still need more confidence and faith. I lack the determination these give. I
am aware of my gifts, but they are nothing without enterprise behind them.
Otherwise they are mere ornaments, or worse, they are lies—of no value to
the world or myself. They must give birth to something worthy. I must see
them as means, not ends, and use them as means. For they have, rightly, no
existence apart from some product of their own. To make claims for them on
any other basis is to be false to the world and myself. I can't allow myself the
spurious comfort knowledge of their bare presence affords. I must work hard
with unceasing attentiveness. I must guard against fear, inertia and uncon-
sciousness in living. I must fight these with all my strength. I thank God for
the knowledge given me by F. M. Alexander. The time will surely come
when the world will know what it owes to this extraordinary man.

November 12, 1951

Alexander had seven teeth pulled last week. His secretary called on Friday
morning to tell me of this and to cancel my lesson for that afternoon. He said

Mr. Alexander was in fine spirits, but they thought it best that he have a few days' rest from his teaching.

So today when I met him for my lesson, I said I hoped that he was feeling better after the ordeal of last week. He said: "Oh yes, thank you, I feel fine. I have nothing to complain about. People usually expect a man of my age [82] to be quite done in after having seven teeth pulled all at the same time, but it didn't bother me much at all."

Then we got on with the lesson. After only a few minutes I felt the lower part of my torso shift backwards as it had done once before. It happened so suddenly, taking me by surprise, that I laughed, and Alexander asked me why I laughed. I told him, and he said: "It's shifting to where it should be, and it does so precisely for the reason that you were not doing anything."

However, this lesson proved to be a difficult one. And at one point I could see that Alexander was deeply serious with me, concerned about my interference just at the point of rising from the chair. This last minute interference has so far proved a stumbling block, for, in spite of myself, I still keep on trying to get up. My feeling is that Alexander cannot possibly get me up out of the chair, even though I *know* from experience that he can, and so I react by wanting to help him, or so I tell myself. He knows this and tells me I must get rid of this idea. I know this and yet I persist in "trying-to-do." Well, in one way I'm glad of the difficulties, for if I ever do teach this work, I shall know what to expect at the worst from my pupils.

November 14, 1951
This past week I've felt restless. To be on a ship bound for lands and people strange to me—this rather than confine myself to a comfortable flat in London. But then the thought of my study with Alexander chases away the fantasy. Actually, I feel impatient with myself; I want to plunge into something, to commit myself to a line of action. I waste time looking for answers inside my head. I lose the feeling of confidence and grow depressed.

But, my dear boy, get hold of yourself. You are not alone. Remember your thoughts of a few hours ago; how all your friends, family, people you love and have loved, and who love and have loved you—they, all of them, though thousands of miles away, can be brought to your side by a mere thought, a mere memory. Truly, an ocean means nothing, or mighty little, when it comes to this.

But what has this to do with my feeling of confidence, of losing it?

Simply that, in part at least, you lose confidence in yourself when you begin to feel too alone in the world. This feeling oppresses you. You feel juxtaposed to the terrible world. You lose sight of the fact that all the people who have ever meant anything to you, miles though they may be from you, are always with you. Just summon them, and they will come at once.

Yes, I see what you mean. Of course, that was my thought too a few hours ago.

Indeed, my dear friend, who does not recoil upon himself if he imagines he stands alone in the world? And besides, another thing to change the subject a bit, don't forget you are engaged in learning and applying the Alexander Technique, which means, as you well know, unlearning just about everything you have learned or acquired instinctively and even much you have learned consciously. You must recognize what it means to experience change as you are now beginning to experience it. This means, as Alexander's friend Rowntree expressed it, "passing from the known to the unknown."[54] This is wonderful and at the same time a little frightening. Keep this thought in mind for you will know more or less what to expect.

But that is true of life also, is it not? Going from a known present to an unknown future?

Of course. And this shows the peculiar relevance and value of Alexander's teaching for the human creature. It equips us to live in a constantly changing world. If man does not change (and does not pass from the known to the unknown) in his manner of reaction, then he will remain forever bound to his familiar, known, instinctive habits of reaction. And this means that man will be outstripped, out-paced by his environment. Indeed, does not the social, economic and technological web of life seem to move and evolve with a momentum of its own while we, man, on the psycho-physical plane, seem to evolve not at all? So we must, as Alexander says, make the transition to life on a more conscious level. It is an evolutionary step we must take, a step we must allow ourselves to take.

November 15, 1951
Good lesson. I feel vastly encouraged. Alexander answered my questions at length. I asked him if the *thinking* that one should do is supposed to be *preventative*. He answered:

"Yes, the thing is, you want to keep the preventative, inhibitory idea in mind *as* you act. You see, the inhibitory idea becomes the primary means of the volitionary act."

Alexander then stepped back a few paces, held out his left hand and extended the index and middle fingers, and said:

"For the sake of argument, say these two fingers represent the old habitual track. You receive a stimulus from within or without the self to do something, for example, sitting back in the chair. And you give consent to this idea—the message goes down this old track. But now, if you do *not give consent* to the stimulus to 'sit back in the chair,' the message stops here [pointing to his knuckles]. Then after withholding this consent, you prepare a *new* track [Alexander now extended his fourth and little fingers] which represents the new means whereby of allowing the neck to be free, the head to go forward and up, and the back to lengthen and widen [primary control]. This is the main idea, you see. You don't care a jot whether you sit back in the chair or not. *That is not important.* But, you allow your head to go forward and up and move back from the hips just a fraction thus widening the back. What results, finally, is the development of a new track, a new line of communication. This becomes a new habit, one consciously formed and maintained. You are bridging the subconscious and the conscious. The subconscious is the old way of doing, a way of doing you never learned consciously but acquired without any awareness at all. And so, you can see how your great compatriot, Dewey, could say that this is a 'revolution in thought and action.'"

> ...it is essential to understand the difference between the habit that is recognized and understood and the habit that is not. The difference...is that the first can be altered at will and the second cannot. For when real conscious control has been obtained, a "habit" need never become fixed. It is not truly a habit at all, but an order or series of orders given to the subordinate controls of the body, which orders will be carried out until countermanded.
>
> (MSI, p. 52)

"As everyone knows, this is the greatest thing the human creature is capable of, that is, the changing of his own reaction."

> ...probably the greatest problem that is still unsolved in the education and development of mankind is the problem of the control of human reaction,...
>
> (UCL, p. 95)

> No matter in what field of activity it is desired to bring about changes, whether so-called physical, mental, or spiritual, the carrying out of the task demands from us a decision to make that fundamental change in the guidance and control of the working of the mechanisms which is inseparable from change in the manner of use of the self, and unless this is taken into account by those who may be responsible in

the future for ideals and plans for individual and social reform, they are not justified in believing that these will prove more beneficial than those which have been found wanting in the past.

(UCL, p. 98)

To make sure of fundamentals once again, I asked Alexander: "When you tell me to let my head go up and out of your hands, should my response to that be *not to do anything?*"

"That's right. You only *allow* your head to go up, and it *will* go up. I'll give you a written guarantee of that. You take care of this point, and I'll do the rest."

———————————

A word of explanation is needed here. Alexander answers this question affirmatively and emphatically so. However, it often happens that the pupil in complying with the "order" not to do anything (inhibitory act) forgets to attend to the all-important matter of directing his use. In a footnote on page 13 of *The Use of the Self*, Alexander says:

> When I employ the words "direction" and "directed" with "use" in such phrases as "direction of my use" and "I directed the use," etc., I wish to indicate the process involved in projecting messages from the brain to the mechanisms and in *conducting the energy necessary to the use of these mechanisms.* (My italics)

"I will give you a *right experience*. You have to trust me in this. I cannot give you a wrong experience; it's impossible for me to give you a wrong experience. Think what that means. A golfer friend of mine was telling me that all the professional golfers will give you nineteen wrong experiences out of twenty and yet they can teach you to play a fairly good game of golf. But here, when you come to me, I cannot give you a wrong experience. Think what that means to you, what it will mean to you."

> ...it is essential to remember that it is both the psycho-physical experiences of the individual in use and functioning, and those that he gains when he is applying himself as an instrument in his activities in the outside world, which combine to make up his experience in living, and it is this sum total of experience which determines the nature and value of his judgment. ... Man still relies upon an undue proportion of limited and deceptive experiences as a basis for judgment in too many spheres of activity and in regard to too many prob-

lems; and this can account in a great measure for the position in which he finds himself to-day... He has been "wishing" for continued progress, development, and freedom of thought and action, "willing" himself to this end, at one time concentrating upon "physical," at another on "mental" means, and also on "spiritual" means.

But as time goes on his attempts to solve his present-day problems by these means have only served to show their limitations, and he is becoming increasingly aware not only of disaster and confusion outside himself, but also of certain growing disabilities *within himself*...

...he will not have brought about any change in that manner of use of himself which has hitherto tended to lower the standard of his general functioning; and the resultant harmful influence of this will become intensified through any special effort he makes, and remain a retarding and degenerating *constant*, associated with conditions of disorder and complication which are bound to lead sooner or later to other harmful habits of use, and gradually to the development of organic trouble and disease.

(UCL, pp. 101-102)

"When you teach this work, the first important thing you have to do is to teach your pupil to allow himself to be taught. Your pupil has to be able to be taught before you can teach him further. Hardly any of my student teachers can get this idea through their heads. There is one student teacher here, for example, who has been here two years and he is just beginning to get hold of this idea. I try to knock it into their heads, like hitting my hand against a stone wall, but it doesn't do any good to hit your hand against a stone wall."

"There is no difference between the greatest philosopher and a plumber's mate when it comes to getting hold of this work, when it's a question of learning to withhold consent and thus not doing a thing in the old way."

"You know, shortly after the war, the Associated Press in your country sent one of their men over here to see me, to interview me for an article on my work. When he came to see me, I told him that he could never expect to write such an article on my work, that it just wasn't possible. I said to him: 'You can talk to me for six months and you still won't be able to write such an article. You ask your employer to let you have a week or two of lessons with me and then see if you do not agree with me.' He was also covering a meeting of some foreign ministers in London. After the meeting, when I saw him, he said: 'When I saw those men seated around the conference table, I thought of you and your work, Mr. Alexander. No sooner would one of them open his mouth to make a statement on the issue being discussed, than two or three of the others would tighten up, getting set to oppose and argue with him.' Well, this correspondent stayed to have two weeks of lessons with me. He went back to America and never wrote the article."

"When all the business with China was going on and we were worried about Manchuria, I knew our policy would lead us nowhere, that it would end by making us lose Manchuria.55 I wrote a six-page letter to one of our ministers concerned with this problem, in which I forecast the disastrous outcome of the policy we were pursuing, and everything I said in that letter came to pass."

November 19, 1951
Yesterday, on a walk in Hyde Park, I sat down on a bench in front of a giant oak tree which in spite of its enormous weight and size seemed to be surging upwards from the earth's surface, its ponderous branches soaring upwards and outwards into the sky, as if possessing some Alexandrian-like anti-gravity mechanism. I realized what a gross mis-conception we have about ourselves. We behave as if our bodies are so much dead-weight—pounds of flesh hanging on our frame of bones. We just can't wait, as we say, to sit down and take the load off our feet. What a spectacularly different and opposite outlook is conveyed to us by the Alexander Technique.

A child grows and grows, measurably grows to the point where measurable growth seems to stop. I wonder if this growing of the child is measurably interfered with by our gross misconception. With no conscious direction of upward expansion to stimulate the anti-gravity mechanisms, sheer physical growth, on the one hand, and the downward pull and collapsing heaviness of the body, on the other hand, may become warring factions subjecting the child to a variety of debilitating muscular twists and pulls. Alexander's teaching ensures that none of this happens and that the tendency towards growth and expansion of the self will continue into and throughout adult life.

November 21, 1951
If what feels most right and comfortable is more than likely to be wrong—as Alexander maintains and as my own experience so far has shown me—then it might prove useful and instructive to deliberately set out to do something in a way that does not feel right and comfortable but rather feels wrong.

The harder one tries to perform a given act, the more certain he is to fail if his performance is characterized by misuse and misdirection of the self. Why is this? Because the harder one tries the more pronounced or exaggerated becomes the misuse and misdirection. Furthermore, the very idea of trying to do something suggests a call for greater effort and energy than normally required to do the thing in question. In other words, the proper "means-whereby" of accomplishment is being ignored. Alexander calls this "end-gaining." In such a case, the best advice is to stop trying-to-do and then to think out the proper means-whereby of preventing misuse of the self, and, finally, the proper means-whereby of performing the given act.

If a person wants to appraise his own conduct in order to find out where it is taking him, he should stop and examine his present activities and then imaginatively project them into the future to see where they lead. For, as so often happens, our present activities may turn out to have no relation whatever to the ends we have in view.

November 22, 1951
Concerning "bad" habits. In *The Use of the Self*, Alexander mentions the habit of smoking and the kind of usual end-gaining efforts to stop. He says everyone knows that each cigarette smoked is a stimulus to smoke another. Therefore, each time we can withhold consent to light a cigarette, we break a link in the chain that binds us. This chain-like character applies to many of our habits, both good and bad. To first recognize the chain is a step toward breaking links in it. For example, every time we put off doing a thing we know we should do, we lay the groundwork for putting it off again. Each drink we take is the stimulus to take the next one. Each strain on the WC is a stimulus to strain again.

Straining on the WC is a wonderful example of end-gaining. I am convinced that it has an effect opposed to the one desired, possibly blocking the rhythmic working of the large intestine or colon. My problem in this matter is rather acute. My doctor in Ridgefield, Connecticut, said I had a "spastic colon." I think he is right. I wonder if it is a result of bad use of myself in the past or if it is a "natural" defect for which I am not responsible. (I was writing this in bed, in the morning, and this writing about it sent me running to the WC where I again had a large BM[56] with spasms; and the accompanying succession of cramps.) Actually a definite change in my bowel habits has been taking place over the past two to three weeks. During this period every BM, with one or two exceptions, has been accompanied or rather accomplished by spasms or cramps. The spasms are in every way similar to vomiting spasms. This has been going on daily—though occasionally I skip a day following a particularly violent discharge. The result, of course, has been that—for what seems to be the first time in my life—I have been cleared out for many days running. I no longer accumulate, over a period of five to ten days, a vast mass of waste material.

November 24, 1951

At the end of today's lesson Alexander said this was my "best lesson" so far. At the start of it he had said:

"You know, I do envy your back, but for God's sake use it. I'll tell you a little story about this 'For God's sake use it.' Years ago, I knew a chap, Clarence Holt was his name, a director of plays. He was an Irishman and wonderful old fellow. He always picked his casts for specific qualities they had. During one of his rehearsals he was trying to exhort a woman to play her part with more gusto. He said to her: 'Madam, you must get emotion into this part, please be emotional.' She tried again, but he was still dissatisfied. He said again, 'Madam, please, we need your emotions in this part.' He pleaded and pleaded. She tried again. Finally he shouted at her: 'Madam. You have the finest pair of breasts I've ever seen. For Christ's sake, HEAVE 'EM!' So whenever I see someone with an asset like your back, and I want to plead with him to take advantage of it, I think of old Holt saying to that actress, 'For Christ's sake, Heave 'em!' Yes, that fellow would say anything."

"You have come to a point in your lessons where you have to have faith in the principles of the work and faith in me. I can feel you hesitate. You doubt that the thing will work. But yet you *know* that it does work. Put your faith in it and don't hesitate. We can never expect to do a thing if we begin by doubting that we can do it, isn't that so? And it doesn't matter at this stage whether or not you are doing it right."

"Six or seven places in my books I have made a remark which no one ever seems to remember, and that is that *ends come of themselves.* When you sit down you are in too much of a hurry to do so. You drive right for the end. Don't think about the end! Don't think about sitting down! What you do want to do, however, is to think of the *means-whereby*, of the means that are right for you to attain the end. The ends come of themselves. They cannot help but come of themselves."

> ...man tends to become more and more a confirmed end-gainer, one who too often insists on gaining his end by any means, even at the risk of disaster, rather than take time to consider means whereby the end can be gained so as to ensure best possible result.
>
> (UCL, pp. 95-96)

> Only time and experience in the working out of the technique will convince him [the pupil] that, where the "means-whereby" are right for the purpose, desired ends will come. They are inevitable. Why then be concerned as to the manner or speed of their coming? We

should reserve all thought, energy, and concern for the means whereby we may command the manner of their coming out.

(UCL, p. 85)

At one point during the lesson while I was "sitting" in the chair, Alexander guided me so that I was poised far forward in the chair. Then he asked me: "How does that feel to you? Does it feel strange?" After a moment's thought, I answered: "I'm really not sure how it feels." Then he gently pushed my head backwards a little, and, at that moment, I felt my back arch inwards. I immediately exclaimed: "Ah, that feels more natural." To which Alexander responded: "But you see, my boy, that is precisely what you don't want to do to yourself. The way that now feels natural to you is the wrong way."

> ...in our conception of *how* to employ the different parts of our mechanisms, we are guided almost entirely by a sense of feeling which is more or less unreliable. We get into the habit of performing a certain act in a certain way, and we experience a certain feeling in connextion with it which we recognize as "right." *The act and the particular feeling associated with it become one in our recognition.* If anything should cause us to change our conception, however, in regard to the manner of performing the act, and if we adopt a new method in accordance with this changed conception, we shall experience *a new feeling* in performing the act which we do not recognize as "right." We then realize that what we have hitherto recognized as "right" is wrong.
>
> (CCCI, pp. 82-83)

"That is what so many people are doing to themselves all of the time. [Alexander, demonstrating, clenched his hands and pressed the knuckles of both hands against each other, showing me how the vertebrae of the spine crush into each other when the back is arched unduly inwards rather than lengthening and widening.] If people would only stop doing *that* to themselves they would not be likely to get things like sciatica or coronary thrombosis."

> ...I look to that wonderful instrument, the human body, for the true solution of our difficulty, an instrument so inimitably adaptable, so full of marvellous potentialities of resistance and recuperation, that it is able, when properly used, to overcome all the forces of disease which may be arrayed against it.
>
> (MSI, p. xvi)

Alexander's favorite quotation:

"What a piece of work is man: how noble in reason! how infinite in faculty! in form and moving how express and admirable! in action how like an angel! in apprehension how like a god!" (*Hamlet*)[57]

November 26, 1951

A stumbling block in my case to concerted activity, to persistence in the doing of what I want to do, is my tendency to see the activity itself as an end and not as a means to something else. This is end-gaining, of course, in a different form, the emphasis lying on the thought or plan of action rather than action itself.

The thought of oneself in one's own little room is stultifying. One needs to keep in mind one's participation in the surrounding life, in the lives of others, in the world of things and happenings.

I am occupied, increasingly of late, though it seems to have been going on for as long as I can remember, with the task of getting to the bottom of myself. At the moment I look upon myself as a mystery and I need to unravel it. For the last day or so I've had the uncanny feeling that the key, if there is one, is just now within my grasp. I feel as if I'm blind and feeling around with my hands. In any case, I will have to wait.

Anthony Eden said to the U. N. General Assembly: "We must deal with small definite problems" in order to make the kind of progress we desire to make. And he said we must also call a halt to futile arguments and dissensions. I thought this a wise speech.[58]

But to come back to myself, which would seem to be my *only* interest these days, I must continually remind myself of the same necessity, to deal with the small, definite and immediate problems and not to plunge over the horizon with ideas and plans only possible over the long run and then only after many small definite steps have been taken. Yes, I have plenty to do right here, in my own backyard.

November 27, 1951

Why should I write, anyway? Why do I sometimes feel so much that I want to write, feel that I can write, once I sit down to it? And then why does it happen that I cannot sustain the impulse? This has happened in the past. It suddenly seems strange that I can't answer these questions. Is there something wrong in my *asking* them? Do I unwittingly, or unconsciously, try to defeat myself by asking them? If I'm not sure of my own motives, desires, impulses to action, does this perhaps signify a distrust of them? Alexander said to me last time: "You have reached a point where what you need now is faith in the work, faith in me." Maybe this is a clue. Maybe what I really need is faith in myself. It might be that my evaluation of my own past behavior is such that I defeat myself in the present. At another time, Alexander had said: "To teach this work, you have to first teach the pupil to allow himself to be taught." Seemingly, there's a connection between these two remarks. I should say to myself: Don't allow any self-evaluation of past failures and false starts to stop you from going ahead now, and in the future! For indeed, are you not changing now? Trust in these changes. Recognize that any new faith you get is itself a change!

December 8, 1951

This week I have devoted at least 85% of my waking time to the Alexander Technique, practising it and just plain thinking about it. Result: good lessons and making progress. And also, every day, reading chapters in *Constructive Conscious Control of the Individual*. Yesterday, in my lesson, I realized that I haven't really been carrying out the act of inhibiting—perhaps the most important part of the whole business. I think this is why I've felt slightly stalemated and discouraged the past few weeks. Either you make the decision to inhibit, or you may as well give up all thought of changing from a bad to a good use of yourself. I see this clearly now. One has to discover and rediscover that improved use follows inhibition with mathematical precision.

In speaking of the education of the subconsciousness below the reasoning plane, Alexander writes (*Man's Supreme Inheritance*, p. 20): "The important point is the fact that the phase of being with which we are dealing becomes, as we progress through life, a composite of animal instincts and habits acquired below the plane of reason either by repetition or suggestion." Indeed, how many of the things I have done so far in life have been done as the result of "habits acquired…either by repetition or suggestion"! I was reading over my "thesis" last night, for the first time in four months, and I truly got a shock: what a mess of words, I thought, meaning what?

Certainly one of the main obstacles to improving the practice of inhibition is the hurry with which we perform so many acts in our daily life. We could help ourselves counteract this by intentionally slowing down our movements. I've found that it is easier to inhibit when moving about in slow-motion.

January 1, 1952

I begin the new year reading Norbert Wiener's *The Human Use of Human Beings*, and I am struck by the relevance of Cybernetics to the Alexander

Technique.[59] I believe they may both have something of importance to say to each other, though I see this "something" only vaguely at the moment. Cybernetics also points up the value of Korzybski's General Semantics as the science of sending and receiving unambiguous information.

Here is an interesting passage from *The Journal of Eugéne Delacroix*:[60] "We should do everything calmly and only react emotionally to great works of art or noble deeds. Work quietly and without hurrying. As soon as you begin to sweat and get excited, be careful. Slack painting is the painting of a slacker." (p. 19, Phaidon Press, 1951)

January 2, 1952
First lesson of the new year and an excellent one. I think the interval of two weeks without lessons was a time for assimilation and consolidation of ground covered and preparation for the new.

During this lesson I felt as if there were a big mainspring in my back and hips. Alexander barely touched me with a finger and I seemed to spring forward and up!

But I still try to get up! However, I think I've reached a point where success in this respect is just around the corner. I do think I am on the point of making new progress. I'm ready to make a jump ahead. I am confident of this.

At one point in the lesson, I said to Alexander: "I couldn't help but feel that it was impossible for me to get up from that position." Alexander's reply struck home:

"Ah, my boy, you see you give yourself away completely with that remark. You see, you *will* try to get up! You just will not leave it all to me. Don't care if you don't get up. It's not your business whether you get up or not. I sometimes, as a joke, tell my pupils that they insult me when they persist in trying to help me get them up [out of the chair]. Getting you up is my job. All I want you to do is to pay attention to your neck and head, so that your neck is free and your head will go forward and up. Now, to stand up, let your head go forward and up. Don't care a jot whether you get up or not, that's my business. Now, head forward and up! That's it. Now, come back to my arm, come back to my arm…"

Of this and other phrases used by the teacher, Alexander makes the following comments in Chapter IV, Part II, of *Constructive Conscious Control of the Individual*, followed by explanations of each of the phrases ordinarily used in teaching:

>…it is necessary to use certain phrases employed in the teaching

technique, phrases which I consider call for comment, seeing that they do not always adequately express my meaning and that, furthermore, they cannot be defended as being demonstrably accurate. ... but with a teacher present to demonstrate in person what he means by them, they serve their purpose. (p. 108)

Of the phrase "Head Forward and Up," Alexander says:

> This is one of the most inadequate and often confusing phrases used as a means of conveying our ideas in words, and it is a dangerous instruction to give to any pupil, unless the teacher first demonstrates his meaning by giving to the pupil, *by means of manipulation*, the exact experiences involved. (p. 109)

The phrase "come back to my arm" reminds the pupil not to go forward in the chair but to allow his back to go back and widen as it lengthens.

Of the phrase "Widen the back," Alexander writes:

> This instruction rivals the last one [Head Forward and Up] in its shortcomings, when considered as a phrase for the conveyance of an idea which we expect a pupil to construe correctly, unless it is given by a teacher who is capable of demonstrating what he means by readjusting the pupil's organism so that the conditions desired may be brought about.
>
> "What really occurs is that there is brought about a very marked change in the position of the bony structures of the thorax—particularly noticeable if a posterior view is taken—also a permanent enlargement of the thoracic cavity, with a striking increase in thoracic mobility and the minimum tension of the whole of the mechanisms involved. (p. 109)

January 6, 1952

I often worry about doing a thing *before* I do it, with the result that I fail to act. I must call a HALT to this timid worrying! I know full well that only in action, in doing and in working, am I happy. My stopping to worry and consider and consider is perverse. A result of fear. Have faith, and act! Though not unconsciously. An unconscious plunge into action is as much a result of fear as fearing to plunge. By all means, be conscious of taking the plunge. Then you can be confident of the outcome.

Life is never a matter of shrinking! Life is a matter of *expanding*, of embracing. Life is growth, everywhere. To live is to grow and to grow with increasing awareness of growing. Don't be afraid of a new idea. To contract, to shrink, to establish and then cease establishing, is tantamount to dying.

What man needs is a change in his direction. Alexander's work is a means for bringing about this change in direction.

January 7, 1952
Had a good lesson with Alexander this afternoon. More and more I have the sensory experience of going "forward and up."

January 10, 1952
As I left Ashley Place today, Alexander said: "One of your best lessons." I, on the other hand, had thought to myself all through the lesson: This is one of my worst lessons—I'm doing so badly!

At one point, Alexander said: "You don't think enough. That's what worries me."

"What the world has to see, and what it eventually will see, is the *effect of the manner of use upon function.*"

> It has not been realized that the influence of the manner of use is a *constant* one upon the general functioning of the organism in every reaction and during every moment of life, and that this influence can be a harmful or a beneficial one. It is an influence for ill or an influence for good in accordance with the nature of the manner of use of the self in living, and from this there is not any escape. Hence this influence can be said to be *a universal constant in a technique for living.*
> (UCL, p. xxxvi)

> From my long experience I can now assert with confidence that the underlying cause of our personal and social difficulties will persist until we adopt "means-whereby" which will not only *prevent* the children of our time and of the future from developing a manner of using themselves that is a constant influence for ill in everything they do, but, in those cases where harmful conditions are already present, will restore a manner of use which will be a constant influence for good. This remains true no matter what other means for alleviating them are adopted.
> (UCL, pp. 9-10)

Today I took my friend Mr. J. for an interview with Alexander. I had told the latter previously of J.'s position with the Outward Bound Trust and described its work, after which Alexander replied:

"I'm in hearty agreement with the out-of-doors, the fresh air side of it, but not with the strenuous exercises, and so forth, for one month. You take these boys out of the city for one month and subject them to thirty days of vigorous exercise, and they will go back to the city worse off than they were in the beginning. Why give them a training they don't need and will never use again? Boys should be educated for what they are going to do, for the kind of life they will eventually live."

But of what avail are good hygienic conditions, an outdoor life, a greatly improved environment, "free activities," and "physical exercises," whilst the child that is to be given an "all-round development" under these conditions is actually allowed to use himself during his activities in ways which interfere to such an extent with the psycho-mechanics of his respiratory processes that these are working nearer to their minimum than to their maximum capacity, and this in spite of the fact that his teachers would unanimously agree that the proper working of these processes is the most vital element in the child's development?

The almost universal call for physical drill, or physical exercises, in schools, for training in posture, breathing exercises, etc., coming from parents, teachers, and all concerned, is an admission that there is a great need in this direction, but, unfortunately, these methods will not give the necessary help. The harmful effects of the child's psycho-physical experiences, gained whilst at study, cannot be remedied by the performance of the movements involved in any forms of exercises, drill, posture, callisthenics, etc., for the defects resulting from these daily psycho-physical experiences are the manifestations of a badly adjusted and imperfectly co-ordinated machine, guided and controlled by a delusive sensory appreciation, and therefore functioning much nearer to its minimum than to its maximum capabilities.

The problem is further complicated in that there has been and still is a continual increase in the educational demands which are being made upon the child, unavoidably, it is supposed, in the present stage of civilization. For the increase in the degree of mal-co-ordination present in the child continues in the same ratio as the difficulties to be overcome in any attempt to eradicate defects, whilst at the same time the degree of difficulty which the child will encounter in connexion with its lessons or other activities will be in accord with the degree of imperfect general functioning. This again means that the child, to ensure success, must of necessity devote more and more time to these subjects, with the result that increasing demands are being made upon him, involving longer hours of work and increased effort, and the increasing complications these imply. How can the psycho-physical mechanisms of the children meet these demands satisfactorily, when they are functioning much nearer to their minimum than to their maximum possibilities? And what is to happen if the educational de-mands continue to increase, whilst the psycho-physical possibilities of the children continue to decrease, as they surely will, unless the defects which make for badly co-ordinated use of the psycho-physical self are eradicated, and instead there is set in motion a process of genuine development on a plane of conscious control in the use of the organism?

(CCCI, pp. 70-72)

I said that my friend has his heart and soul in his work, that he is a firm believer in rigorous exercise, but that he is one of the most tied-up, rigid persons I know. Alexander said:

"Ah, yes, that's the way it goes. A man should never teach others unless he has lived and experienced what he teaches."

"You always get people who immediately want to teach. I ask them: 'Why? Why do you want to teach?' The trouble is that they want to try to change or help others without themselves being changed or helped in this way."

Most children at school manifest defects in the use of themselves in the ordinary acts of life—in a large number of cases, very serious defects—and all kinds of drills and remedial exercises are employed in the attempt to eradicate these defects. Yet, except in very rare in-stances, the teachers employed in these remedial and other spheres in our schools are too often themselves beset with exaggerated forms of the same or other defects or peculiarities. If teachers are worthy of the name, it is certain that their pupils will be influenced by them in more ways than one, and that most pupils will tend subconsciously to imi-tate them. ... A realization of the serious consequences involved in the foregoing will bring conviction that all teachers who manifest defects and peculiarities which are the result of their own unreliable sensory appreciation and unsatisfactory use of their psycho-physical organism are a bad example—indeed a positive danger—to their pupils, and that the possibility of satisfactory psycho-physical results accruing to both pupil and teacher is seriously minimized by this impeding factor—viz., the acquisition of defects and peculiarities by imitation.

(CCCI, pp. *158-159*)

January 12, 1952
I read Time magazine this afternoon (Saturday), then went to the 5:30 movie at the Classic on King's Road to see *Edward and Caroline*[61] for the second time. There was also a short film on *Rubens* that I particularly desired to see.

Returned hastily to flat to hear a BBC performance of Schoenberg's *Gurrelieder*[62]—it's been all of seven or eight years since I heard it last, from my own recording of it, the records I lent to a girl friend to keep for me while I was in the Navy, and I never got them back from her. I listened absorbed and moved to tears at the passages that I used to play again and again while writing poems.

I bought the Phaidon edition of *The Journal of Eugéne Delacroix* and began reading it this evening. It has over 80 plates. It promises to be absorbing reading.

Tonight I again have a feeling of certainty about myself and my desire to paint, to learn how to draw and to paint. Yes, I am confident that I can soon learn to paint competently if only I can succeed in harnessing my moods—I realize that every mood, every state of mind, feeling, etc., that tries to inform me of futility, insuperable obstacles, inability to persevere, and so on, endlessly, is tantamount to a withdrawal from life. It amounts, ultimately, to saying: "Well boys, even though we have lived hardly more than three decades, it's time to throw in the towel. There's no point in going on, because we won't get anywhere anyway." How utterly stupid this attitude is—as if life is not meant to be lived *at this moment!* Forget about 10, 20 or 30 years from now—that day may never come, so why throw today away because you fear an uncertain day far ahead in the uncertain future? That isn't even sensible! Furthermore, it's just one more classic example of what Alexander means by end-gaining!

I'm also beginning to realize much more fully another difficulty in my outlook towards work and life: it is this—I tend to resist doing the necessary work, the practice and training required of any profession. I actually seem to think, in effect anyway, that I don't need to go through all of that. My dreams skip over it all, to place me upon the throne at the end! Well—this is, again, end-gaining. I suspect this is a disease peculiar to our time. We all are in too much haste to be Somebody. Nothing is intrinsically wrong with wanting to be Somebody—nothing is more human in a human society! But it's wrong when you act as though "dreaming will make it so."

Of late I have become convinced of one thing: that *achievement* and *confidence* are two sides of the same coin. Remember Alexander's remark: "Life is the development of conscious control and confidence!" And I came across this sentence by Delacroix: "…nothing is so rare as the confidence which alone can beget great masterpieces." Confidence means really a readiness to live literally rather than to die figuratively.

January 14, 1952
A wonderful, most wonderful lesson. As I was taking leave of Alexander, he said: "That was very good today. You are coming along all right now."

Nevertheless, all was not clear sailing. So often a "good" or "wonderful" lesson means the contrary of being free and easy and simple as the following remarks of Alexander during this particular lesson will show:

"There, you see! You will try to go forward, in spite of all I say! You *will* try to go forward! BUT THAT'S YOU! YOU DON'T STOP! You are too anxious to *do* something! That's the trouble with us all; somebody tells us to do something and we act at once! We are all trained that way. The father tells his son to do something, and the boy jumps! It happens like lightning, that reaction to a command or impulse. What we have to learn to do is to inhibit this first immediate reaction. As soon as you are able to do that, you are automatically at liberty to do something else, to adopt, that is, some other course of action."

> I have already pointed out that children from the first moment of school life onwards manifest a lack of inhibitory development, and the fact that in most cases they learn to obey orders at once, without stopping to consider the "why and the wherefore," is a contributing factor to this harmful condition.
>
> (CCCI, p. *102*)

"You see, it doesn't matter, it does not make any difference whether you go forward, go back, stand up, or not. *Let me take care of that!* It makes no difference here whether you are right or wrong. You have only one thing to do: to see that you do not tense your neck, to allow your head to go forward and up, thereby obtaining a widening of the back, an expanding of the chest, you can never burst a blood vessel or contract coronary thrombosis—so many thousands of people in Britain die every year from that one disease alone, and I imagine it is the same in your country."

My experience in all these cases has brought home to me the close relationship which exists between the manner of use of the mechanisms and the standard of functioning, for where I have found unsatisfactory use of the mechanisms, the functional trouble associated with it has included interference with the respiratory and circulatory systems, dropping of the abdominal viscera, sluggishness of various organs, together with undue and perverted pressures, contractions, and rigidities throughout the organism, all of which tend to lower the standard of resistance to disease.

(*UoS*, p. 61)

"There, you see—if I do your thinking [inhibiting] for you, then you work beautifully."

"It is good to not try and get a thing right the first time. Sometimes, I actually start out by doing what I know to be a wrong way of doing and then, *in the process*, I set it right..."

...under orthodox teaching methods, the teacher expects his pupil to try to be "right" from the very start in carrying out whatever he is asked to do, and the pupil also believes in this idea and acts accordingly. In expecting this of his pupil, the teacher is not only asking him to overcome at one stroke the influence of long-established habits of use, but also to accomplish this feat while being guided by the unreliable feeling which had led him into his wrongness.

(*UCL*, pp. 80-81)

This last remark made me think of learning to draw. When the student first begins drawing from the model, he unfailingly tries to get his drawing *right*, from the very first touch of his pencil to the paper, with the result that he stiffens and torments his line. I have found in my own drawing these last few days that it helps not to care whether I get it right—or not.

I shall always remember the following remark, the way he said it:

"This work is so simple, you know. The trouble is, it's too simple."

Indeed, we might say that a dangerous stage of perversion and delusion has already been reached, when the attempts at solution of all the problems of life seem to call for complexity rather than simplicity in procedure. We even reach a stage when the most simple "means-whereby" in accomplishment become the most difficult. A very interesting instance in this connection occurred in my teaching experience. A well-known man of scientific attainments had great difficulty for some days with a simple, practical problem of psycho-mechanics concerned with his re-education. When he came to his lesson one morning he said: "I know now what is the matter with us all. This work of yours is too simple for us!"

(CCCI, p. 7)

Apropos of that, Alexander related how a well-known professional man had said to him: "You know, we have all these things like psychoanalysis, but you have the answer right here, in all its simplicity."

> The method of psychoanalysis, therefore, like other methods of treatment on a subconscious basis, is an instance of an "end-gaining" attempt to effect the "cure" of a specific trouble by specific means, without consideration being given to the necessity of restoring a satisfactory standard of general psycho-physical functioning and of sensory appreciation.

(CCCI, p. 58)

The following quoted paragraphs are from a letter written by John Dewey, dated May 22, 1918, to an unidentified critic of Alexander. The contents of this letter were made available to Eric D. McCormack, whose Ph.D. dissertation, "Frederick Matthias Alexander and John Dewey: A Neglected Influence," is my source for the paragraphs.[63] According to Mr. McCormack, this letter is "in the files of the Alexander Foundation (London),[64] but the name of the addressee has been withheld."

> All of the 'psychic' complexes have their basis in organic dis-co-ordinations and tensions, with compensatory flabbinesses, and his technique is a technique for resolving and unravelling these, reducing the present technique of the psychoanalyst to an incidental accompaniment, and cutting out the elaborate ritualistic mummery with which the present psychoanalysts have been obliged to surround their method. In addition, Mr. Alexander's technique unravels the kinks and complexes by a process of positive replacement in which sound co-ordinations are built up with their corresponding alterations in habitual sensory and emotional data, while at the best the psychoanalysts merely untie a knot and leave the organic causes which produced it untouched.
>
> Before I had lessons myself, although I had talked with him

[Alexander], read his earlier book, and members of my family had had many lessons, I argued against what seemed to me prejudice on his part against psychoanalysis, on the ground that in principle his method was similar. Only after I had had experimental demonstration did I see how completely right he was in saying that their method was negative, and left the patient subject to the same thing in some other form. ... I have written at some length, although I realize that to you this is all probably a matter of argument and opinion, while with Mr. Alexander and with those who have had the good fortune to get inside his principle or method it is a matter of sheer fact; he is the only person I have ever known, or known of, who knows what he is talking about in the sense that a competent engineer knows when he is talking about his speciality. (From a letter by John Dewey)

Before I started Alexander lessons with the Barrs in April of 1950, I had made brief stabs at drawing and painting, such as doing portrait sketches in charcoal of most of our friends who spent weekends with us in South Salem. Whether this desire to draw and paint was because of a history of such in my family—my grandmother, mother, sister and brother painted more or less seriously from time to time—or because my Jungian analyst, Dr. Abel, encouraged me to do so, I don't know. What I do know is that my Alexander work opened me up to the possibility of doing serious work in this field.

Such were my sporadic efforts in drawing and painting up until the time I started work at the Heatherley School of Art in London in January of 1952. When I entered the teachers training course I stopped going to Heatherley but nevertheless vigorously pursued what by that time I regarded as a serious avocation on my own. At some point in 1954 I started working in clay. The first thing I did was a bust of Alexander from photographs. It turned out rather well even though firing in the kiln caused many small cracks on the surface, giving it an interesting texture. I painted it with acrylic white, glazing the red-brick color of the fired clay, the terra cotta. I never showed it to Alexander, nor, for that matter, this diary of my lessons with him. I regret both omissions; it would have been good to have his comments.

January 17, 1952
I stopped in a pub and had three beers. Standing at the bar, I experimented with "balancing" myself, strongly emphasizing the direction to my head. What I experienced was a *pull* forward and up that seemed to originate from

the direction of the head itself. The sensation was as if my head was pulling me up.

January 21, 1952
Yesterday, January 20th, was Alexander's eighty-third birthday. Today's lesson started out badly (according to my own estimation) and ended well. Alexander said he disliked having to use the word "try." I must learn to inhibit!

"You convert this step of inhibition into the primary activity of freeing the neck, allowing the head to go forward and up, lengthening and widening the back, expanding the chest, and so on."

During this lesson I noticed a very sudden release and expansion in my breathing.

Part of my difficulty is that *I am always trying to be right!* I must stop this trying to be right, for immediately I try to be right, then, willy-nilly, I do things wrong, i.e., in the old way that feels right. I must cease this trying to be right! Inhibit this tendency and I shall then be free to project the guiding orders, that is, to direct my neck to be free, my head to go forward and up, etc. Moreover, if I can inhibit this tendency, which is so overwhelming, to try and be right, I can then allow *nature* to assert itself!

January 23, 1952
This morning I got up at 5:30 to write down a vivid dream (in other journal). Did drawing at Heatherley from twelve to six o'clock. I'm making progress I think. The past two days I've felt a little depressed. I must not be faint-hearted! In the past I've given in far too easily to feelings of discouragement, mainly of self-doubts. I must realize that all or most men have such doubts—yet they persist, and go on with their work. I must think less of the future which tells me nothing, and only depresses me—and make the most of the present. After all, I am living now. Otherwise, the whole of a man's life is one long preparation for some consummation that may never come. Life is meant to be lived *now. Do now* what you *plan to do.*

January 27, 1952
The last two days this week at Heatherley, I've used Conté crayon, rather than pencil, in my drawing—F. Wynne Thomas came around for the first time on Friday. He looked at my day's work in drawings, and praised them. He explained carefully the interior shadow of volumes, using illustration of a billiard ball. I found this helpful and enlightening. He said that you have to be careful with Conté crayon because "your drawing can look better than it

really is." I had recognized this, and emphatically agreed with him. He said you can get nice results with it. He looked at one of my drawings, and said I had gotten a nice quality in the shading. Later he brought me an old drawing of Frederick Whiting's to show me, illustrating what he had said about the billiard ball.

January 28, 1952

Got to Heatherley's by 10:00 and did two drawings, about half an hour for each—the model being a red-haired student, very round face, strong body, wearing a black dress and green stockings, with a scotch plaid kerchief wound about her neck, and fixed in front with a silver clasp. She was interesting, and I drew her with enthusiasm in Conté crayon, being very free. MacNab passed by, stopped by to look, but offered no criticism.

January 31, 1952

I had a rather amusing dream last night, so today I related it to Alexander:

"I was giving a lecture on the Alexander Technique to a group of students back in my old prep school. During the lecture I drew on the blackboard a diagram of the lungs. The figure represented the lungs as two horizontal fat sausages. I said to the students: 'Believe it or not, that sausage-shaped figure represents the lungs.' Then I drew a profile of the skull and the spinal column. But in order to represent the latter it was necessary for me to trace the chalk off the blackboard, down the wall, and all the way down to the floor, thereby indicating the length or lengthening of the back. The long horizontal sausage-like lungs were meant to indicate the width or widening of the back."

Alexander laughed and said: "That shows you are really absorbing what I teach you."

Then I told Alexander how, so often, when I awake in the morning, my neck feels as though I had been tensing it to the utmost all through the night. He said:

"Yes, people ordinarily are never aware of what they do to themselves in their sleep. As someone said to me once, 'People die in their sleep.' With myself, it is impossible for me to do such things to myself even during sleep. For as soon as I do something like that, it hits me like a bolt of lightning—I immediately become aware of it. When you lie down to sleep, you ought not to lose the awareness you have in your waking hours. Before dropping off, give yourself the orders for the head to go forward and up, the back to lengthen and widen, and so on."

So far as investigation has been possible, it has been found that people often tend to exaggerate in sleep the harmful manner of use they employ during their waking hours. It is not generally appreciated that although the need of activating the mechanisms responsible for the process of living may perhaps not be so great during sleep as during the waking hours (because of the generally lowered tone and tempo of the functions), it is nevertheless present, and may be interfered with by the same harmful habits of use as prevail in wakeful activity.

(UCL, p. l, footnote 1)

At one point in this lesson Alexander gave an unusually firm forward-and-up direction to my head with his hands. The consequence, for me, was an unusually acute awareness of my head going forward and up out of his hands, of lengthening. Alexander said:

"There, you felt that? If I had done that in the beginning of our lessons, you would have *pulled down* on me."

I said to Alexander: "I was realizing the other day that the head, when free to do so, actually exerts a pull on the rest of the body, a pull upwards. For it seemed to me that I experienced such a pull very strongly a few evenings ago as I stood at a bar drinking a glass of beer and projecting the orders." He answered:

"Yes, indeed. That is just what the head does do. Soon you will experience this pull constantly. You will have it all of the time, and you will feel strange without it! When you get that, you are on the road to Tipperary."

This lesson was a very good one, and, in a way, I regard it as a milestone in my progress. I had gone into this lesson, on the way to Ashley Place, aware of various tensions and un-doing them. During the week I had become aware in particular of a more or less habitual tensing of stomach muscles, and I found this to be definitely associated with the "pulling-in" of my lower back. For stopping this tension not only had the effect to some extent of allowing the lower back to "shift" backwards, but also seemed to increase the freedom in breathing. However, all this was secondary to the awareness of what I was doing with my head and neck.

February 1, 1952
Got back to flat and resumed working on a landscape, a composition subject for next week. Started it last night and made a horrible mess. So I got depressed, doubting my ability, distrusting myself, once again. Again, the faint heart! First sign of messing things, I weaken and cringe! I must have a remarkably high idea of my ability if, when I fail to paint a masterpiece at the

first stroke of my brush, I begin to doubt myself. Who am I, that I should not botch things and make a mess? Here I am, trying to paint *pictures*, already! I haven't yet learned how to handle paint properly. The drawing goes so well I doubtless expect my working with paint to be equally happy. Foolish fellow!

As Alexander says to me, I *will* try to be right! I shall and must rid myself of this fool's habit. Even MacNab says to his students, "Don't try to get the thing right!" And I heard Thomas tell a student, "We're not here to paint pictures, but to learn how to paint."

February 4, 1952
Another excellent lesson. I now think I am securing a definite grasp of the work. However, there is one thing that continues at this stage to be the crucial obstacle: When Alexander tells me not to try and stand up, nor to even think about standing up, I nod in agreement, and I resolve not to do anything in the way of standing up. But, when the crucial moment (my use of the word "crucial" is significant!) comes, I *do try* to stand up! I try to help Alexander as he takes me out of the chair, and this in spite of all he has said and all my intentions *not* to do so!

Thinking about this now, I suspect that part of my difficulty is this: I am too anxious to succeed in this work. I insist upon thinking it important that I get up out of the chair!

> Another incentive to end-gaining on the pupil's part is his desire to gain in a given time the maximum benefit from his lessons irrespective of the conditions to be changed. Unfortunately for him, in view of the nature of his educational training, this very commendable desire causes him to make a special will-to-do effort in his desire at all costs to be "right." But as his "right" is wrong, this merely means a stronger effort in the wrong direction and an exaggeration of his habitual way of "doing" the very things he must get rid of, if he is to gain the improvement he desires.
>
> (UCL, p. 85)

Now, let's see: if I *don't* get out of the chair—that is, if Alexander is *unable* to take me up out of the chair, this means that I am pulling down (pulling backwards and downwards), i.e., actively interfering with the primary control of use, tensing my neck, not allowing my head to go forward and up, and, in fact, *shortening rather than lengthening!* Here is the point: this *interference* means that, in spite of what I think or believe I am *not* doing, I am actually

Tom Mott, Bill (P. E.) Williams and Goddard Binkley in St. James Park, London, 1953. (Photo by Anthony Spawforth).

Goddard Binkley in 1986, outside Paris

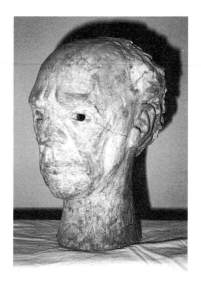

F. M. Alexander, bust by Goddard Binkley, 1953

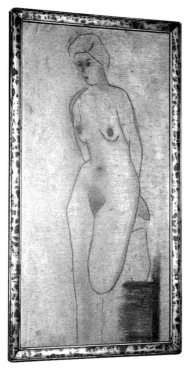

Woman Sitting,
skulptor, 1 9 5 6

Untitled, black crayon sketch of
girl, similar to the one exhibited
at the Artists of Chelsea
Exhibition, May 1 9 5 3

House and Barns, oil on canvas, exhibited at Artists of
Chelsea Exhibition, May 1 9 5 3

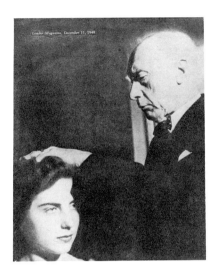 

F. Matthias Alexander teaching, photos from the article The Man who
helped Sir Stafford Cripps , Leader Magazine, December 1948

Ashley Place and Westminster Cathedral, London, 1950. (N° 16 is marked with an arrow)

trying to get up, and this trying-to-get-up actually *prevents* me from getting up! It follows, even logically, that if I *do not try* to get up, I *will* get up. Conclusion: *Trying-to-do interferes with doing.*

> ...all "trying" starts from some personal conviction that in some way we shall be able to do what we are trying to do, and this conviction, like conviction on any other point, is made possible only by virtue of impressions received through the agency of our sensory processes. ...if the functioning of our sensory make-up is unsatisfactory, our register of what is happening in response to the stimulus to "try" is likely to be deceptive, so that the reaction we register is more than likely to be different from the reaction that has actually taken place.
>
> It seems strange to me that although man has thought it necessary in the course of his development in civilization to cultivate the potentialities of what he calls "mind," "soul," and "body," he has not so far seen the need for maintaining in satisfactory condition the functioning of the sensory processes through which these potentialities manifest themselves.
>
> (UoS, pp. 78-79)

Alexander tells me time and again not to care a damn whether I get out of the chair or not, because he knows that this "not caring" (in this context) implies a refusal to end-gain and thereby allows *him* to take me up out of the chair with the least possible exertion on his part and allows *me* to experience a "correct" use of myself.

Alexander said today that we could put the matter this way—after I had prevented him from taking me up by trying to help him, which sounds utterly paradoxical, but I can testify to the utter truth of it!—he said:

"You can even try to *prevent* me from taking you up. Put it that way, if it will help you."

> ...doing what feels wrong is paradoxically associated with a gradual improvement in the pupil's general use and functioning.
>
> (UCL, p. 87)

"You see, once you get hold of this idea, once you can *carry out* your decision to inhibit, then there is nothing you cannot change in yourself in the matter of old habits. But if you or I were to tell people this, they would think we were mad. You see the point, don't you? Even with the great men I have had among my pupils, none of them were able to stick to a decision to not do a thing, a decision they made two seconds before."

"Now, I will not try to take you out of the chair if you try to help me. No matter what you do, of course, I can get you out of the chair. But, you see, I don't want to do it if you try to help me. You must leave everything to me. I'll do the work, and if we don't get up, care not a jot. Some of my student-teachers here will insist upon taking a pupil out of the chair even when the latter tries to help them, which they should not do, of course. But I won't take you up if you try to help me, because I don't want you to get out of this chair unless you are going to have a right experience in the process. And you will have a right experience if you stop thinking about getting up. *Don't think about getting up!*"

February 7, 1952
A superb lesson! I went determined to make the decision *and to stick to it!* And was rewarded. If all continues to advance from this point, I shall be indeed, as Alexander said, on the road to Tipperary.

One has to *have* this marvellous experience in order to believe it. But even then, as I know so well, faith in the belief may not come easy.

Aldous Huxley writes, in his *Ends and Means* (1937):

> Mr. Alexander has given a full account of his system in three books… It is therefore unnecessary for me to describe it here—all the more so as no verbal description can do justice to a technique which involves the changing, by a long process of instruction on the part of the teacher and of active co-operation on that of the pupil, of an individual's sensory experiences. … A verbal description would mean something only to a person who had actually had the experience described; to the mal-co-ordinated person, the same words would mean something quite different. Inevitably, he would interpret them in terms of his own sensory experiences, which are those of a mal-co-ordinated person. Complete understanding of the system can come only with the practice of it. (p. 223)

John Dewey, in his introduction to *Constructive Conscious Control of the Individual,* opens with the following paragraphs:

> The principle and procedure set forth by Mr. Alexander are cru-cially needed at present. Strangely, this is the very reason why they are hard to understand and accept. For although there is nothing eso-

teric in his teaching, and although his exposition is made in the simplest English, free from technical words, it is difficult for anyone to grasp its full force without having actual demonstration of the principle in operation. And even then, as I know from personal experience, its full meaning dawns upon one only slowly and with new meanings continually opening up. Since I can add nothing to the clear and full exposition that Mr. Alexander has himself given, it has occurred to me that the most useful form this introductory word can take is an attempt to explain wherein lies the difficulty in grasping his principle.

The chief difficulty, as I have said, lies in the fact that it is so badly needed. The seeming contradiction in this statement is just one instance of the vicious circle which is frequently pointed out and fully dealt with in the pages of the text. The principle is badly needed, because in all matters that concern the individual self and the conduct of its life there is a defective and lowered sensory appreciation and judgment, both of ourselves and our acts, which accompanies our wrongly-adjusted psychophysical mechanisms. It is precisely this perverted consciousness which we bring with us to the reading and comprehension of Mr. Alexander's pages, and which makes it hard for us to realize his statements as to its existence, causes, and effects. We have become so used to it that we take it for granted. It forms, as he has so clearly shown, our standard of rightness. It influences our every observation, interpretation, and judgment. It is the one factor which enters into our every act and thought.

Consequently, only when the results of Mr. Alexander's lessons have changed one's sensory appreciation and supplied a new standard, so that the old and the new condition can be compared with each other, does the concrete force of his teaching come home to one. In spite of the whole tenor of Mr. Alexander's teaching, it is this which makes it practically impossible for anyone to go to him with any other idea at the outset beyond that of gaining some specific relief and remedy. Even after a considerable degree of experience with his lessons, it is quite possible for one to prize his method merely on account of specific benefits received, even though one recognizes that these benefits include a changed emotional condition and a different outlook on life. Only when a pupil reaches the point of giving his full attention to the *method* of Mr. Alexander instead of its results, does he realize the constant influence of his sensory appreciation. (pp. xxi-xxii)

February 11, 1952

Alexander confirmed today, of his own accord, my feeling that I am on the verge of securing a firm grasp of this work, a firm grasp of the *principle*; that I am on the verge of being able, of *allowing* myself, to put the principle into practice. This feeling has been strong the past two weeks.

At the end of the lesson, Alexander said: "You're on the brink now!"

His words excited me, and I told him how I had been feeling so strongly of late that this was, indeed, the case.

When I entered his study at 12:30 today, he was warming his hands before the coal fire. He still had his spats on, and he kept them on during the lesson. On cold, damp days like this one, he likes to move his teaching-chair in front of the fire and conduct his lessons there. Thus, facing the hearth, I could enjoy looking at the little *objets d'art* on the mantelpiece while having the lesson.

As I stood in front of the chair, Alexander said: "Now, let your head go up and out of my hand, and let the knees go forward and away from one another."

"You see, the entire *natural* movement of the spine is upwards, of the head is upwards. But as soon as we pull our heads back, we frustrate that natural activity of movement upwards."

I asked Alexander: "But does that [pulling our heads back] still apply to the times when we have to pull back our heads in order to look up, say, at a tall building?"

Alexander stepped around to stand in front of me and said:

"Ah, you see, my boy, when I do *that*, I don't *shorten* myself in order to do it. First *lengthening*, and *then* to bring the head back so that we may direct the eyes upwards. But, you see, most people, when they do this, shorten themselves in looking directly above them."

Several times, then, Alexander gave me the experience of lengthening and then gently tilting my head back so that I looked directly at the ceiling, during which I observed a complete absence of that stiffening of the back of the neck that one usually feels (if aware of it at all) in pulling the head far back in order to look upwards.

I said to Alexander: "I was looking at an anatomy book recently and noticed that the trapezius muscle sends two big cords up the back of the neck, extends outwards to the shoulders, and shoots down the back. Is it this muscle that we ordinarily use in pulling back the head in such a way as to counteract or frustrate the natural upward activity of the head and back?"

Alexander answered this question in a way that told me that the matter of how individual muscles functioned was of no particular interest to him. He said:

"What is important about the muscles for me is their total working together—how they all work together in order to accomplish the lengthening and widening we want to obtain. Your question reminds me of a famous physiologist who said to a friend, while the two of them were watching me demonstrate on a pupil: "Look at that! Here we know all about each and every muscle, what each one does and is supposed to do, and look at what Alexander is doing there!""

> The physiologist may know the names of the muscles and the particular function of every one of them, but in the matter of employing them to the best advantage in a unified working of the human organism in daily life, this knowledge does not help us very much.
>
> (UCL, p. 112)

> ...[Physiology] *does not and cannot indicate the means whereby these muscles are operated relatively to the individual's use of his mechanisms as an indivisible unity, so as to ensure that integrated working of the organism which we always find associated with the standard of functioning present in a person in whom the way of employing the primary control is a constant influence for good.*
>
> (UCL, p. 115)

"You see, all that the large muscles of the neck are supposed to do is to turn the head on its own axis and to tilt the head forwards and backwards and sideways. The trouble comes when we try to do with these muscles in the neck what we want to do and are supposed to do with the muscles of the legs, the arms, and so on."

"So, in our work, it's not just a question of relaxing the neck. That is the wrong point of view. The point is to *stop doing with the neck* what needs to be done *only* with the arms or legs, etc."

> One can recall the expression or interest, happiness, and satisfaction exhibited by the child when one has enabled him to understand for the first time that his unduly stiffened neck—with perhaps his head too far pulled back—is really not the fault of his neck at all, but is due to the fact that he is trying to do with the muscles of his neck what should be done by other mechanisms.
>
> (CCCI, pp. 181-182)

87

> Let us take for example the case of a man who habitually stiffens his neck in walking, sitting, or other ordinary acts of life. This is a sign that he is endeavouring to do with the muscles of his neck the work which should be performed by certain other muscles of his body, notably those of the back.
>
> (*MSI*, p. 57)

After quoting several passages in the Bible that attribute bad conduct to being "stiff-necked," Alexander said: "Yes, it's all there."[65] He quoted again St. Paul's remark: "That which I would do, I do not; that which I would not do, I do." He went on to say:

"When I read that, I thought it was one of the most tragic statements ever made. St. Paul was an extremely religious man, so anxious to do the right thing. But, you see, in spite of all that, it was of no help to him. He had thus to admit that tragic truth. And it is the same with all of us, you see. We see the same thing every day all around us. How many of your friends are ever able to stick to their fine resolutions? People want to give up their bad habits, habits that they know are bad for them. Yet, no matter how hard they try, they never succeed. But here, in our work, this is precisely what we are doing. When you come here, you are acquiring the very means-whereby that will enable you to change any or all of your habits."

> The truth is that so far man has failed to understand fully what is required for changing habit if the change is to be a fundamental one, because he has not realized that the establishment of a particular habit in a person is associated in that person with a certain habitual manner of using the self, and that because the organism works as an integrated whole, change of a particular habit in the fundamental sense is impossible as long as this habitual manner of use persists.
>
> (*UCL*, p. 76)

> A good manner of use of the self exerts an influence for good upon general functioning which is not only continuous, but also grows stronger as time goes on, becoming, that is, a *constant* influence tending always to raise the standard of functioning and improve the manner of reaction.
>
> (*UCL*, p. 5)

"In the beginning of my work, I did not know whether I would or could teach what I felt to be the truth. I used to say to my earliest pupils: 'Now tell me whatever you think is wrong in what I am doing to put things right according to the principle that I believe to be the truth.'"

"You see, I've never approached my work and teaching with the view that this is all, that this is the answer and nothing more remains. As I said to Dewey one day: "I want to be proved wrong." If we go to work teaching something with such an idea as this, that there is nothing more than this to be said—how shall we ever discover anything more? But in all my years of teaching, nothing about my principle has been proved wrong or scientifically refuted in any way. And I know that nothing ever will be."

...my experience may one day be recognized as a signpost directing the explorer to a country hitherto "undiscovered," and one which offers unlimited opportunity for fruitful research to the patient and observant pioneer.

(UCL, p. xxxvii)

I have in daily lessons for nearly fifty years demonstrated to pupils and others the influence for good or ill of this constant upon their general functioning, and the fact that repetition of the demonstration is possible provides that kind of proof of the soundness of concept and principle, and of the technique, plan, or method based upon it, which is acceptable to the scientific engineer when he finds that in working to a concept or principle he can build a machine that, as a working mechanism, satisfies the need for which he designed it.

(UCL, p. xxxvi)

It has not been realized that the influence of the manner of use is a *constant* one upon the general functioning of the organism in every reaction and during every moment of life, and that this influence can be harmful or a beneficial one. ... Hence this influence can be said to be *a universal constant in a technique for living.* (*Ibid.*)

"When I teach, I teach the principle, I never forget that. Some of the younger teachers today tend to ignore the principle, to try and accomplish the work by means that ignore the principle."

My experiences...convinced me that in any attempt to control habitual reaction the need to work to a new principle asserts itself, the principle, namely, of inhibiting our habitual desire to go straight to our end trusting to feeling for guidance, and then of employing only those "means-whereby" which indirectly bring about the desired change in our habitual reaction—the end.

(*UCL*, p. 25)

"Long before George Bernard Shaw became acquainted with my work, I wrote him concerning something he had written about learning to ride a bicycle. I told him that the first time I rode a bicycle, I rode for miles without falling off. Today, bicyclists tie their feet to the pedals—that's a result of my work. I explored the right means for the action of pedalling. [Here, Alexander demonstrated what he meant, sitting on a stool next to the chair and moving his feet in bicycling fashion. As he did so, I found myself marvelling at the free and generous movement of the legs made by this man of eighty-three years.] What we so rarely do is to examine the means whereby we may accomplish a particular act or deed."

"When we set out to do a thing, getting it done is not the really important thing. Rather, what is, above all, important, is to pay attention to what we are doing to ourselves while in the process of doing that which we set out to do."

March 10, 1952

After my last lesson a month ago, I went with friends on a three-week holiday, skiing, two weeks in St. Anton and a week in Zermatt. Being my first time on skis, I joined a beginner's class. After two days I was moved to a more advanced one. It's a marvellous sport. I got the feeling that nothing else mattered in the world but skiing.

I was depressed getting back to London. My friends said this was usual after being in the mountains. But seeing Alexander again was a great help. I saw him on March 6, and then today. During today's lesson he said:

"In you, the difference between sinking down, pulling yourself down, and allowing yourself to go up, is enormous. As I have said to you before, your back is so strong and powerful that if you are doing the wrong things with it, you do the wrong things twice as badly, you do twice as much damage to yourself, as the next fellow. You have enough strength there in your back to lift ten men your own size, if you allow it to work properly."

"I wish I didn't have to use the words 'standing up' and 'sitting down.' For they convey the old way of doing things. In standing up, for example, we don't just stand up and stop there: we go on with the activity of the head going forward and up, coming back to widen the back, allowing the ribs to contract and so on."

Expanding ideas are the forerunners of human advancement. The conveyance of the knowledge concerned with expanding ideas, whether by the written or spoken word, calls urgently for the recognition of the fact that expanding ideas demand new words which will adequately express the original as well as the new thought or thoughts involved.

(CCCI, pp. xiii-xiv)

In October 1951, about a month after I arrived back in London after my European tour with Anne and Paul, I met a Swiss girl, Gita Irminger, at The Linguist Club near Belgrave Square where I was taking French and German classes to get a reading knowledge of these languages to fulfil a requirement for the doctor of philosophy degree. Gita was from Zurich, studying fashion design at an art school in London. We were both living in Chelsea—she as a paying guest in the home of an English family on Burnsall Street off King's Road; I in an apartment about half way between Sloane Square and the river Thames. My lease expired in March. Rather than renewing it, Gita and her adopted family invited me to move into their home as a paying guest. The family were Daisy Swanson and two daughters, Peggy and Jane, who worked as secretaries. A third daughter, Bobby, lived and worked in Rome. Daisy had lived most of her life in Vienna as the wife of a wealthy Jewish banker. They fled to London when Hitler annexed Austria, losing just about everything but their lives. Daisy took a job as a cashier in a restaurant. Her husband sold books in a used-book store for a few years and then died. Daisy was a marvellous cook, and Gita and I were treated as members of an expanded family.

March 13, 1952
Alexander told me of an occasion when he was asked by John Dewey to visit a "progressive" school in America.[66] He watched a psychologist working with several of the children. All of them exhibited a poor manner of using themselves. After the children left the room, Alexander asked the psychologist what it was he had done. The psychologist said he had observed the children carefully in order to make a judgment about their behavior and their potentialities. Alexander asked: "But how can you form such judgments when their use of themselves is obviously as bad as it is? How can you determine what their capacities and potentialities are when they are not able, under the present circumstances of their poor use, to properly manifest them? You wouldn't judge the performance of your car if you knew there were certain mechanical deficiencies in the engine."

I asked Alexander: "You mean that before judging the present and the prospective abilities of these children their poor use should be set right?"

"Exactly so," he said.

> Where the imperfectly co-ordinated child is concerned, its first need is to be readjusted and co-ordinated on a plane of conscious control, until the standard of functioning in psycho-physical use of the organism is adequate. The organism will then function as near to the maximum as is possible, and the potentialities for improved functioning will continue as the child gradually develops to that standard of conscious guidance and control in psycho-physical use which makes for the conditions essential to the fullest development of latent potentialities.
>
> (CCCI, p. 137)

I said to Alexander: "There are two particular activities in which I notice a very definite tensing of my neck—eating and speaking." His answer was as follows:

"Very likely you are not tensing up but rather unduly relaxing, sinking down instead of going up, like this. We can't trust our feelings in these matters. So often a pupil complains to me that his legs are painfully tense. But I feel his legs with my hands and they aren't tense at all. I place the pupil's own hands on his legs, and he then sees that his feeling about them was wrong."

I then asked Alexander: "I've been wondering if perhaps the untrustworthiness of our feelings in respect to more or less physical processes in our bodies has any kind of parallel in, or extension to, our feelings in respect to other people?" He said:

"Yes, indeed. For we know how often the judgments that people make of one another are false or misleading judgments."

> In consequence of the unreliability of his sensory impressions, man's interpretation of his own and other people's experience in living is too often faulty and illusive, and he is liable to arrive at false conclusions, and to form erroneous judgments, especially where the motives for his own and other people's behaviour and general activities are concerned.
>
> (UCL, p. 97)

I asked Alexander how old George Bernard Shaw was when he had first come to him for lessons. Alexander thought for a moment, and then said he was seventy-nine years old. He went on to say:

"When Shaw came to me, he was suffering from angina, and he could scarcely walk from here to across the street. He had to go a snail's pace, lest his heart trouble him. But in three weeks of work with me, he was walking heartily from here to his hotel."

March 17, 1952

A fairly good lesson, though it didn't quite fulfil my expectations. Alexander recommended a play, *Nightmare Abbey*,[67] at the Westminster Theatre, just a few blocks from Ashley Place. "Good acting, good laughs, a lot of philosophy," he said.

Alexander will teach until the end of July. He goes for holiday during August, returns in September. He said London is not a good place to be during August.

March 24, 1952

Alexander said he thought this lesson would prove of value to me because we had cleared up some points by talking them over. He said never to hesitate to ask him questions on things not clear to me.

His answers to my questions in this lesson were more or less what I expected them to be. What I gained from them was confirmation and eradication of some doubts. I particularly wanted to hear his answer to the following question: "In freeing the neck, in allowing the head to go forward and up, in lengthening and widening the back, and so on, we should make no attempt to *feel* these changes?" Alexander answered as follows:

"No. That's just it, you see. If you attempt to feel, to rely on your sensation of feeling, you can only revert to your old habitual way of doing. If we attempt to *feel*, we cannot help but *do in the old way*. The supremely important thing to remember is that here we are not interested in *doing* anything. As I have said before, we are not trying to be right. This is the principle of the whole work: *not to do something but to think!* We redirect our activity by means of thought alone. This principle is the hardest thing of all to grasp. People just don't see it. Yet we know that it works. It is demonstrable."

"When I teach you, I am giving you guidance with my hands. I don't want you to do anything. Don't try to be right. Leave everything to me. Except that you should be *conscious of the experience* you acquire under the direction of my hands, and that you, through thinking, *allow* yourself to be taught. That is the particular problem of the pupil: he must give me a chance to teach him."

The employment of inhibition calls for the exercise of *memory* and *awareness*—the former for remembering the procedures involved in the technique and the proper sequence in which they should be used, and the latter in *the recognition of what is happening*. In the process both potentialities are developed and the scope of the use of both gradually increased. Moreover the experiences thus gained not only help in developing and quickening the recalling and connecting memory, but cultivate what I shall call the motor-sensory-intellectual memory.

(*UCL*, p. 93, my italics)

"What we are doing is laying down new lines of communication. If I tell you to 'stand up,' and you react immediately to this, you will react according to the old lines of communication—which means, among other things, a stiffening of the neck and a pulling back of the head, and so on; all totally unnecessary to the act of standing up, and not only unnecessary but also *interfering* with standing up, so that we must needs expend excessive amounts of energy in order to overcome that negative tension and pull. On the other hand, if, instead, when I tell you to 'stand up,' you then say to yourself: 'No, I won't stand up,'—then this refusal inhibits your old customary reaction and thereby allows a *new* line of communication to be laid down, namely, the means-whereby of lengthening and widening, etc."

March 27, 1952
Right after the start of this lesson, Alexander asked me to "stand up" but *not* to give consent to this idea. Then he said, "Now, to stand up, allow the head to go forward and up, and come back to my arm…" The result was that I found myself sitting, or rather leaning, forward (!) in the chair, instead of standing on my feet. In other words, I had given consent to the idea—stimulus, order, command, suggestion, request, etc.—of standing up, thereby *interfering* with the primary control of my use, with the result that the difference between me and a block of stone was of little practical importance. Alexander stopped, stepped a few paces away from the chair and, turning, fairly shouted at me:

"There you are, you see. That's you! You can't get away from you! It's you—and you can't get away from it! You will try to get up!"

April 7, 1952
I went to this lesson thinking that it would not be a particularly good one. This was because I had felt during the week more or less stresses and strains, "physically." But, as usual, my feelings (which so often pass for thinking)

were wrong. During the week I had thought a good deal of two principles: *Not to try to be right* in anything I was doing, whether painting, talking or thinking of the "means-whereby;" and, secondly, *not to rely on my feelings*, not to trust any information they might give me. I started to write—not to rely on my feelings in respect to the matter of allowing my neck to be free, head to go forward and up, back to lengthen and widen. But I stopped myself because I had already included this, the "means-whereby," under the first principle, not to try to be right. This little incident has startled me into the realization that we are dealing here not with two principles but *one* principle. For it follows, as much as night follows day, that if you rely on your feelings, if you insist on relying upon them (in spite of your previous decision to the contrary), you are trying to be right! The reverse is equally true: if you try to be right, you are not *just* relying on your feelings but forcing yourself to rely on them!

As I said, my feelings were wrong in anticipating what sort of lesson I would have today, for it was, in fact, a good one. Alexander started me "standing up" and "sitting down" very soon after the lesson had begun; it was quickly obvious that, today at least, I was not interfering.

Non-interference is another way of looking at inhibition. I think it is a good term, for it expresses the idea that anything you *try to do* WILL result in interference with what Alexander is attempting to convey, i.e., the particular experiences associated with the primary control or the manner of use. So you might say to yourself: "I will not interfere with Alexander's teaching by trying to do what I think is right or what I think is the right thing to do."

Alexander again stressed how important it is to grasp the principle of *non-doing*. He said he had racked his brain for a long time over the question of what was the best way to get this idea across to his pupils.

> As long as we continue to react in "doing" according to our familiar habit of use, we, *by our own doing*, make change of use and reaction impossible.
>
> (UCL, p. 25)

> In my work we are concerned primarily with non-doing in the fundamental sense of what we should *not do* in the use of ourselves in our daily activities; in other words, with preventing that habitual misuse of the psycho-physical mechanisms which renders these activities a constant source of harm to the organism.
>
> (UCL, p. 106)

And Alexander said again, as he had said so many times to me: "As soon as people see that something has gone wrong, they immediately start to *do* something to put it right. They feel they *have to do*, failing to realize that it is their very own habitual ways of doing that put the thing wrong to begin with."

> It is what man *does* that brings the wrong thing about, first within himself and then in his activities in the outside world, and it is only by *preventing* this *doing* that he can ever begin to make any real change. In other words, before man can make the changes necessary in the outside world, he must learn to know the kind of doing he should prevent in himself, and the HOW of preventing it. Change must begin in his own behaviour.
>
> (MSI, p. v)

Lest we get the wrong idea: it is not doing, in itself, that is wrong, needless to say. The idea is not to become a passive, inert lump of humanity. On the contrary, the idea is to become an active, free, poised, *live* human being.

It is a question, in other words, of transforming doing-which-interferes with the working-integrity of the self into doing-in-accordance with the working-integrity of the self. In order to achieve this, it is necessary, *essential*, to *stop* doing and to stop all idea of doing (inhibition) *for a time*. For only by *stopping* can one succeed in *registering* the experiences that lead to the transformation: to doing-in-accordance (volition) with the working-integrity of the self.

April 10, 1952
A good lesson. At its conclusion, Alexander said:

"Your best lesson so far. This was the kind of lesson I like to give, where I can see my pupil understanding his mistakes and visibly profiting from them."

At the beginning of the lesson, I was certainly interfering, not keeping to my decision to inhibit, to *allow* rather than *do*. But, for most of the lesson, I did succeed in keeping to this decision and thus "again" experienced the wonderful ease and effortlessness of this pattern of movement (from sitting to standing). I put "again" in quotes only to indicate that the right experiences gained in each lesson are never (and cannot be) precisely the same as those in the preceding lessons. Nor will tomorrow's right experience be identical with today's. This is a characteristic that is so striking of these lessons: the element of surprise that marks, almost without exception, each one of them. At one point in today's lesson I exclaimed to Alexander: "It goes against all one's ordinary ideas and opinions!"

At the previous lesson I had taken a friend, a woman of great charm and intelligence from a well-known family, along for an interview or demonstration lesson with Alexander. Some years ago she had read his books and was now interested to meet him. I was present all through the interview (lesson), and while it seemed to me that it went well, I was once more impressed with the truth of Alexander's remark that the first thing the teacher has to do is to get his pupil to allow himself to be taught.

Later, during my lesson, Alexander asked me if my friend had had an illness over the last few years, adding that he would have thought so from her general condition. I said to my knowledge she had not, unless "lethargy" were an illness. He answered:

"Ah, yes, indeed it is. One can understand her lethargy from the way she slumped down in the chair, and from the way she stands, throwing her stomach forward and letting it fall."

He said he thought she would profit greatly from lessons. Then he added:

"But she is not a person that one should try and persuade. That would be folly."

Considering the brief time he had spent with her, I thought this a most discerning remark. It expressed my feeling also, for I had already decided I would do nothing in the way of persuading her to have lessons, though I was convinced she would derive enormous benefit from them.

Twice this week, while drawing the model in life class, MacNab has come to me and said: "I think you should do as much painting as you can. It will be your salvation." He continued: "You are line-bound." He thinks I am too concerned with the line of the figure, neglecting the modelling, the roundness of the figure, etc. I think he is right. He thinks that painting will force me to pay more attention to this aspect of the figure. He asked what I had in mind for the future—"portraits, commercial work, or just the artist-at-large?" I said I hadn't given much thought to the future. He said: "You should paint and paint and paint!"

April 24, 1952
First lesson after an interval of two weeks.

I definitely have a new awareness of lengthening. This past week I have become aware of a tendency to push my stomach back (or to pull it in)—perhaps in the mistaken belief that I was thereby allowing my back to widen—and this was accompanied by a slight though distinct "pulling down" in front. I also found that sometimes when I thought I was allowing (directing) my head to go forward and up, I was, in fact, putting my head forward and down, which was probably associated with the tendency to "push my stomach back." All of this, of course, indicates a trying-to-do rather than a non-doing and allowing.

May 7, 1952
A very good lesson.

Alexander said that excessive tension in the muscles tends to produce waste products. Thus a manner of use characterized by habitual tension may be exacerbated by the presence of such products. He spoke of this also in connection with exercises, which so far from doing anything to change or improve the manner of use, may tend to exaggerate the dis-co-ordinations and imbalances already present.

May 19, 1952
A red-letter day! My two paintings have been placed in the exhibition which opens tomorrow! The Chenil Galleries on King's Road. How pleased and happy I am! What a wonderful feeling it is! When I get the confidence in painting that I have attained in drawing, I shall have achieved something. I want to work hard and consistently, but with peace inwardly and confidence. My habit of doubting myself is slowly becoming an anachronism.

May 29, 1952
Another struggle, but perhaps a good lesson all the same.

I realized today, more deeply than ever it seems, that in spite of all I had previously thought and felt, I was not really making a firm or *consistent* decision to prevent my head from pulling back and thereby to allow it to go forward and up. The trouble is, I've been too concerned with "thinking about the end," as Alexander said, instead of the means-whereby.

From this lesson to the end of July I had nine lessons, one each week, for which I made no entry.

July 13, 1952
Have been painting steadily these past weeks. Have learned much from Ray Bethers,[68] painting at Heatherley. Four or five of us work in one room at Heatherley. He helps us all. Ray is an American artist, has published a book on composition, and uses Heatherley as a place to work.

Alexander takes a month's rest at the end of this month. Progress these past four weeks has been good. Unless things change, I plan to resume lessons with Alexander and study at the Heatherley School of Art in September. If so, I will be another year in England.

August 12, 1952
Taking Nuni, our little golden cocker spaniel, with me, I drove from our house in Chelsea, through South Kensington, up Exhibition Road, and through the gate into Hyde Park, parking amongst the line of cars in the car park just past the bridge over the Serpentine. From there, Nuni and I began our usual walk. We walked up to and around the police station and the tea house, passing close to the gate at Marble March. We have done this many times, and each time adds a little increment to my joy and surprise at finding myself in Hyde Park.

You might imagine that Hyde Park would be a joyous surprise to an American like myself, for where, I ask you, in all America, does one find anything comparable, in a city, I mean? New York, of course, has Central Park, a great park. But there is not the quality of *country* that possesses one in Hyde Park. It isn't that you can't escape from the sight of tall buildings surrounding you; no, Central Park just has not the sweep and naturalness of Hyde Park. For example, there is the great plain that runs from Marble March to Hyde Park corner. You get a wonderful view of this plain if you approach it from near the middle of Park Lane. Entering the park you come first to the line of trees. Standing there, on the edge of the park, you look beyond the tree trunks and see this plain sweeping from right to left and away into the distance, with a slight rise in the middle towards Bayswater. What a surprise it is to see this vast green area before one's eyes, while at one's back stands the stone and glass and noise of city life. If you stand there on a day when the air is a little hazy, bluish in the far distance and golden in the middle distance, seeing this plain through the wide dark lines of the tree trunks in the foreground, then you will have this scene spread out before you at its very best.[69]

December 2, 1952
Here in London the fog continues into its third night. The only mode of transportation possible is walking—and that's dangerous if you don't know the area you're in. The *Sunday Times* this morning headlined it "London has worst fog in years." It's not just a clean fog, but a very dirty one. It settles on everything, penetrates doors and windows—it's in your room, where the rays of your lamps shine through it. The fog gets deep in your nose, throat and lungs—makes you cough. We went to a movie around the corner—figures loom up before you—you don't see them before they're two or three feet in front of you. The fog was in the movie house—the screen was blurred, and it

looked like they had a very weak bulb in the projector. We saw a girl stand-ing outside the theatre, under the dim light of the marquee—waiting. We had seen her last night in the Builder's Arms with a soldier in the Grenadier Guards. You can't help but think of all the things that could happen in a fog like this, all unnoticed. You imagine whatever kind of underworld London has, it must emerge in force in the fog. The robbers and the cosh men that London papers are always full of must be having a free and easy time. But the fog is depressing, even though we tend to get used to it. It seems incredible that, if you could use your car, you drive ten miles or so, you would find yourself in the clear clean night, able to see the stars and the moon. What a relief this would be—so refreshing, able to breathe fully once again, because in the fog you automatically try not to breathe too deeply, to keep the stuff out of your lungs.

January 12, 1953

After my lesson of last July 24, now six months ago, I didn't see Alexander for a lesson until two weeks before Xmas. Alexander went north for his annual holiday during August and part of September. Gita and I and Peggy Swanson left for Italy the middle of August and, after two weeks in Zurich with Gita's family, returned to London on October 2. Today is my third lesson and, all told, my seventy-second lesson with Alexander.

I had put off seeing Alexander because my funds were running low after the holiday and Christmas was coming up. But the delay gave me a longer interval over which to test the stability of my new and evolving manner of USE. The result is so encouraging. I have every reason to believe that in respect to my direction and control I am operating on a "new plane." My first two lessons in December confirmed this belief.

With today's lesson, however, I found myself up against the same old problem, as the following remarks of Alexander will show:

"Don't help me to get you out of your chair. You will persist in this, even though you know very well that I don't want you to help. If you want to help me, help me widen your back—come back to my arm. Widen your back. Let your head go forward and up. Let it go on up and forward. Don't think about getting up! As soon as you start to think about getting up, you will TRY to get up, and then you will forget all about the means-whereby and act according to your old habits and be misled by your feelings."

"This is not easy. If you can tell me how I can get this across to my pupils in a better way, you will be doing a great service to mankind."

I do not believe that the experience of today's lesson contradicts my re-mark above: "I had every reason to believe that in respect to my direction and control I was operating on a 'new plane.'" Because it is apparent to me that we are dealing here with a principle and a process of growth and change to which there can be no final state of perfection. The process and practice of the Alexander Technique involves a never-ending passage from, in Rowntree's words "the known to the unknown." Indeed, I believe that whoever engages in the practice of the Technique is taking an evolutionary step.

January 15, 1953

A superb lesson! Alexander said: "That's the best you've done!" I was confident that I would have a good lesson today. In thinking about the work prior to the lesson, I reminded myself again to STOP! to SLOW DOWN! For it is certainly a question of reacting *too quickly* to each and every stimulus to do something, and it makes no difference whether this is a stimulus arising from within the self or one external to the self, inasmuch as, in both instances, the mechanisms involved in the *manner of reaction* must be the same. Obviously, if you do not give yourself enough *time* to put in motion the means-whereby, you make change in your manner of reaction impossible.

> ...there is one phase of the technique and its history which I should like to stress at this time. It relates to the way in which the nature of behavior is determined by the *speed* of response (reaction) to stimuli.
>
> There came a time, early in my career, when I became aware that I was wasting my energy; wasting it, because my too-quick reaction was a serious stumbling-block to me in practically everything I tried to do. How well I remember the words of an old man, the dearest friend of my younger days, "the more hurry, the less speed," and the kindly yet tormenting question of my mother and father, who would often ask me, "Why don't you think before you speak or act?" On one occasion I remember I retorted angrily that it was easy enough for them to ask that question, but impossible for me to answer it. The objective proof that this "impossible" was rendered possible by subsequent experience can be found in *The Use of the Self*.
>
> (MSI, pp. viii-ix)

Such were my thoughts while dressing after my bath this morning, while putting on my shoes, etc., and I remembered Dewey's succinct descriptions of the Technique as "thinking in activity," "a revolution in thought and action." I was struck by the aptness of the former phrase. When "thinking in activity," you maintain awareness of the HOW (manner of use) as well as the

WHAT of your doing. To this there will be some who say: how tiresome, how tedious to be made aware of all this. Isn't life complicated enough?

In a sense, the objection *is* justified. For most people everywhere, their manner of use *is* deleterious, their sensory appreciation *is* inadequate, *is* untrustworthy; and so life is *already* complicated, and then the prospect of an expanding awareness in respect to all the doings and undergoings of the self would appear only to increase the burden. Precisely this is the whole point, the heart of the matter: that most of our judgments, opinions, estimates, about what is and will be, are influenced by what we are, i.e., our manner of action and reaction in daily life. In various ways, Alexander makes this point many times over in his books, and, while the thesis is not new—is even a truism—Alexander has not only described the nature of the influence, he has gone further; he discovered the mechanism in behavior that more than anything else *makes* us what we are, namely, the *primary control* of the manner of use. The *technique*, the procedure of re-educating others and of carrying on the re-education of ourselves (of which this diary is a description and exemplification), is, in a sense, a rehearsal of the steps that Alexander took in the making and demonstration of this discovery.

> As far as we can judge, mankind has not had the experience of thinking in activity where the projection of messages necessary to the employment of the primary control of his use is concerned. In the ordinary way man has just reacted instinctively to any stimulus to activity, whereas in the new plan which I am suggesting the messages, preventive and otherwise, must be consciously projected *in their right sequence* throughout the activity.
>
> (UCL, p. 92)

> ...after some time the pupil can begin the inhibition of the wrong use of the primary control in all the simple and other acts of life, for this is largely a matter of that process of remembering which is involved in "thinking in activity"—a new way of living—and when once he has experienced the joy and satisfaction of this, it is difficult to believe that the old way could be reverted to. The new way of use will have come to feel right while the old way will feel wrong.
>
> (UCL, pp. 88-89)

As I said, this was a superb lesson, and Alexander confirmed it when he said, "That's the best you've done!" The truth is that I made an experiment during this lesson which may, I think, have had something to do with its success. I made a point of more or less directly attending to the movement and placing of Alexander's hands—on my head, neck, shoulders, back, chest, and so on. And it seemed to me that I thereby experienced a readier response, so to speak, to the *direction* his hands communicated to me. I think the explanation for this lies in the fact that, in consequence of paying attention to the movement and placing of his hands, I enabled myself to take my mind off my own feelings, to forego preoccupation with what was happening to me and therefore to resist the temptation to feel what was going on in the usual way. In effect, I put my own particular involvement as an ego off to one side so that I became, one might almost say, a "participant observer"—I did not stand in the way of my own *allowing*.

January 16, 1953
I seem to be really getting Alexander under my belt this week. I tell myself to "stop feeling!" and I shed tensions like a duck sheds water.

January 19, 1953
From the start of this lesson I directed myself to *stop feeling*! For I have concluded that feeling, whatever else we may say about it, is a form of doing. True, it is covert and invisible, and an observer would say that we were doing nothing at all—but perhaps it is *doing*, all the same. This conclusion goes just a step beyond my previous thinking on the subject. Many lessons ago (see entry for *November 7, 1951*) I had what to me was a wonderful experience, an experience that followed upon my more complete realization that feelings and sensations can be misleading, that they were misleading me! With that, I went beyond the mere intellectual understanding of Alexander's assertion that the sensory appreciation associated with an instinctive control and direction of use—at least at *this* stage of man's evolution—is untrustworthy. However, I did not connect feeling or sensation with *doing*, in the sense of performance of an act or a movement. Indeed, I suspect that no matter how quiet and tiny the feeling or sensation there is very likely some muscular activity going on as accompaniment.

What I am attempting to say in the above paragraph comes down to this: that there is very little difference, if any, between trying to do something (as we ordinarily think of doing) and trying to feel something (as we ordinarily think of feeling). The latter is as likely to interfere with conscious direction and control in the use of the self as is the former. In either case, we are trying to be *right*! The result is to interfere with the sensory awareness of experiences that are, in the nature of the case, bound to feel wrong!

During this lesson, all seemed to go well, at first. Alexander followed his usual procedure. He placed his left hand on top of my head, his right hand on the back of my neck and then on the upper part of my back and shoulders, and then his left hand on my side just below the chest—"in order to allow the ribs to contract and expand," etc., etc. And then he repeated the "orders" constituting the means-whereby to, in this case, rise from the chair—and then, "coming back to my arm…" But right here, at this point, I interfered with myself. I did not "rise" from the chair. Alexander said: "There, you see, you are trying to get up!"

In my answer to this comment, I repeated exactly what I had said on a similar occasion many lessons previously when I exposed the stupidity and error of my ways. I realized this as I answered him, but I *had* to say it again because I wanted him once more to drive the lesson home to me, a lesson that is utterly contrary to what ordinary experience has given one to believe and expect. I answered: "But it seemed absolutely impossible to me that I should be able to stand up from the position I was in." He said:

"Well, there you are! You see, by what you have just told me you were not inhibiting the desire to get up. In fact, you were *thinking* of getting up from the chair!"

Of course I saw the truth of this but whether for this or some other reason, I laughed aloud at myself. Alexander said:

"You see, it's all so much a matter of belief and intent. We have to banish these beliefs. The trouble is, we refuse to believe in the means-whereby. If we sat down and traced the beliefs we hold back to their sources, we would find preciously few good reasons for holding on to them any longer."

He then went on to make the following remarks:

"I use my hands as little as possible on my pupils, having cultivated this use."

"I spent hours, days, months, even years, practising inhibition. I had no one standing by my side telling me what not to do. I kept it up, until one day I got up out of my chair without effort of any kind. I just shot right up."

"We cannot progress any further until you succeed in inhibiting the idea of getting up out of the chair. What you should do away from me is to *think these things out!*"

March 17, 1953

Today I spent more time than ever in thinking of the "orders" or means-whereby while sitting in a chair, standing, walking or whatever it was I was doing. The results were immediate and striking. Not the least among them was the entirely different sense that I had of myself. Indeed, when I think about it, I can scarcely remember what it was like to be me at the time I started these lessons.

April 15, 1953
We went to Cornwall for the Easter holidays. The high point of our visit, for me anyway, was our meeting Ben Nicholson[70] and Barbara Hepworth[71] in their studios. Ben Nicholson is a small man, but strongly built and agile on his feet. He wore an orange colored sweat-shirt, the sleeves pulled up to his elbows. His pants were tucked in at the ankles, and he wore sandals. His voice is high pitched but pleasant. His eyes come to a point at their outside corners—blue eyes. His hair perfectly white, bald on top. He said he didn't think one could be taught to paint. He said there was no such thing as "technique" in painting. Before leaving, I bought a small painting titled *Two Circles*, for 40 guineas.

May 10, 1953
On Friday I submitted two pictures to this year's Artists of Chelsea Exhibition—an oil on canvas titled *House and Barns* and a drawing in black crayon of a girl student at the art school. I feel confident they will be accepted. If not, I shall take it as bad judgment of the jury, not as a reflection of bad painting or drawing.

May 12, 1953
My pictures have been accepted, and the private view is tomorrow.

May 16, 1953
When Gita and I went to see the exhibition today, the ticket collector told us that one of my two pictures had been sold! What a wonderful surprise. It was the drawing of the girl student. And what a spur to work! I've been drawing and painting all day, in oil on cardboard—the pieces that come inside the shirts from the laundry.

May 21, 1953
Had my first lesson with Alexander since Easter. He called it my best lesson. "The best you've done." And he agreed to take me into his teachers' training course in June!

The above is my last diary entry. I joined the teachers' training course in mid-June, 1953.

Part III

Notes from the training course

1954–1956

A BRIEF INTRODUCTION

During most of the years of my lessons with Alexander and my teacher training, Alexander's staff included Margaret Goldie, Walter Carrington,[72] Irene
Stewart, and John Skinner. Walter was clearly in charge of the training
course. Irene and John came in on fairly rare occasions, and Margaret, not at
all. And Alexander was now confining his teaching to private pupils. I remember him visiting the training class only once while I was in it, in 1955,
the year he died. Peter Scott,[73] though not a member of the staff at Ashley
Place (he considered himself an "outsider" there—my first hint that Alexander teachers were not all one happy family, which was a little disillusioning
to me in my inexperience and *naïveté*) came to the class every day, giving
Walter valuable assistance in a class of about ten students. Peggy Williams,[74]
well advanced in experience and training, also helped. A few months after
Alexander's death, his staff of teachers and, of course, we students in the
training class moved to new quarters at 5 Bainbridge Street, close to St. Giles
Circus.

The following are the names of my fellow students in the teachers training course from June 1953 to October 1957:

Richard Baldock, Dorothy Corfe, Winifred Dussek, Edward Gellatly,
Anna Haddon, Nancy Krizek, Stewart Law, Liza Lechstein, Jean Macklin,
Ted Peacock, Pat Peacock, Kirk Rengstorff, Anthony Spawforth, Constance
Rooth-Tracey, and (Small) Bill Williams.

———————————•◦•———————————

June 19, 1953
Today ended my eighth day with the Alexander Teachers' Training
School at 16 Ashley Place. And today I became aware for the first
time of doing-tension in my lower back. I think a big obstacle has been
removed.

June 23, 1953
The Alexander work goes well. Yesterday, I had a phenomenal "undoing"—
impossible to describe. I approached a similar state today. Truly amazing!

After class in the afternoon I went to the William Scott[75] exhibition at
the Hanover Gallery and purchased a small gouache in black, white and
greys. Got to talking with Erica Brausen, one of the directors, a pleasant, no-

nonsense, French lady.[76] She agreed to deliver my gouache to me in two weeks time and look at my work. She said I looked more like a sculptor than a painter. She asked, "Have you talent?" Without hesitating I said "Yes!"

June 26, 1953

Peter Scott worked on me today for what seemed like 20 minutes. He said that when I was "directing" my neck to be free and my head to go forward and up, I was trying to do it and forgetting my back which was pushed forward. On the other hand, when I was trying to allow my back to go back to lengthen and widen, I was forgetting my head and neck and pulling my head down. I had been more or less aware of this difficulty from time to time; yet, it seemed like a revelation when Peter confirmed it. So, once again, the important principle is brought home to me that "thought alone" will move the energy necessary for the direction to take place; whereas trying-to-do-by-feeling is self-defeating.

July 10, 1953

Erica Brausen brought my William Scott over, and I showed her my paintings and drawings. She said, "You have great talent, work hard, do as much as you can, and call me from time to time so I can see what you are doing. You have learned in two years what takes others twenty years. But you don't yet have what I would call a signature."

July 17, 1953

Played the piano for an hour before leaving for Ashley Place this morning; this is the longest I've sat at the piano in several years and only the sixth or seventh time I've played at all since leaving America just over two years ago. I remembered the Alexander guiding orders while playing and what a tremendous difference it makes! Rusty as I was, I played with an absolutely unaccustomed ease and facility.

July 26, 1953

A few days ago, after a lapse of several months, I resumed working on my sort of autobiographical novel, *Glensalemdon*.[77] No painting for almost two weeks! I miss not painting, though I think a pause now and then is a good thing. The interval convinces me more than ever that painting or drawing is necessary for my peace of mind and being fully alive.

August 4, 1953

Played tennis today with Richard Baldock and Tony Spawforth, two fellow students in the training course. I hadn't played in four years and was surprised at how well I did. When I got home I had a good session at the piano. Never have I felt such power and certainty in my playing. For the first time in several days I did no painting.

August 28, 1953
I cleaned my room this morning and looked through a pile of drawings. I came away from that with increased certainty of my ability as a painter, as an artist. But I know I have yet to realize myself fully. This is a stirring but peace-of-mind-making thought.

September 7, 1953
I saw Terry Frost[78] in the Leicester Galleries[79] and, conquering the faint heart, reintroduced myself. He said he had recognized but couldn't place me. I asked him to come and see me which he did on Friday. I showed him my work. He mentioned a few things he seemed to like and my fondness for areas of blue. He likes strong color, not weakened with too much white. He described one picture as "bitty." I agreed with him. He thinks Victor Pasmore[80] is the best painter in England today. He mentioned John Wells[81] in Newlyn, Cornwall (Ben Nicholson had suggested I visit him which, regrettably, I did not) and also Peter Lanyon's[82] studio near St. Ives. Frost will be in London until Christmas and is looking for a flat. At the moment he's staying with Patrick Heron,[83] in Holland Park. He said he would call in a few days and invite me over to see his latest work. I hope he does.

September 14, 1953
Today begins the new term at the Alexander school. All were there but no new faces. Had a turn from Walter, Peter, and also John Skinner for the first time. John doesn't usually teach in the training course, being occupied with his work as F. M. Alexander's secretary and his own private teaching. John told me to think more about widening my back in breathing and not to put my chest forward. I also need to think more about *freeing my neck and allowing my head to go forward and up*!

September 17, 1953
Terry Frost called yesterday, and I went to see him at Patrick Heron's house. Roger Hilton[84] was leaving as I arrived. After Terry showed me his latest work, we went to Roger's house and they had me to lunch. Besides Roger, there was his wife, Ruth, and their small daughter, Rose. A couple of hours later Roger came home with me and looked at my work. His remarks in

random order: "Something pleasing about it...hard to criticize...unusual...in a category by itself...linear, all graphic...decorative rather than plastic use of color...really quite like Leger...slightly Klee-like...rather expressionist ...poetic... You paint as the birds sing..."

September 20, 1953
Roger Hilton calls my art expressionist. I think he is right. It explains several things: my liking for black and white, for movement, for a black line. More and more I want to chase strong color out of my painting, which I don't use plastically anyway. Hilton has opened my eyes to this. The expressionist idea seems in line with my attitude towards painting, which is more emotional than aesthetic.

September 21, 1953
The work in Alexander class went very well today. I think I've reached a new level in allowing my neck to be free and in lengthening and widening my back.

I've started to read over the diary of my lessons with F. M. Alexander. I am finding this helpful: it clarifies, enlightens, and confirms!

Last night we saw T. S. Eliot's play, *The Cocktail Party*. It was well acted and totally absorbing. Eliot really makes you think about what he says. And something about this play affected me deeply, both in feeling and knowing: the frustrated desires, the confused family relationships, the having a wish and being granted that wish, and the power of belief. Sir Claude says at one point: "I make a rule to say to myself that I never understand the other man, but yet that he understands me better perhaps than I know myself."[85] That is the great paradox in human relationships: though we can never really understand the other person, we need that person in understanding ourselves.

September 22, 1953
Ken Peabody, from the art department of the University of Florida, in Gainsville, came over and had tea with us this afternoon. Then I drove him to the airport for his flight back to America. He came to London especially to have some lessons in the Alexander Technique. A most likeable man of 29 years, he is obviously ill, though the Alexander lessons were "a great help." He talks as if each and every word is an effort. Each word comes on a sigh of tiredness, as if in utter resignation to something. I urged him to try to continue his lessons in America.

September 23, 1953
John Skinner worked on me and said "Don't lock your hips!" I begin to realize that one of my more pernicious habits is to lock my pelvis forward, thereby pulling in my lower back and tending to collapse or drop my stomach.

October 26, 1953
I was impressed once again today by how unreliable our sensory appreciation can be. The experience of what you are doing with your body is so often contrary to what you are really doing (as shown in a mirror, for example). We have to face up to this fact and give up relying on our sense of feeling and decide once and for all to rely on conscious direction and control. Here is the difficulty. For thirty years my "feelings" have decided what's right and what's wrong for me. They, my "feelings," have told me how to do things, like sitting down in a chair, talking with a friend, making love or painting a picture. Of course, the point is not that feelings are bad and that we must live without them, as if that were possible. The point is rather that our feelings must take a less exalted place in the hierarchy of our behavior. We must learn to observe and accept our feelings but only within the context of our ongoing conscious direction and control. Within this context our feelings and emotions will tend to be more just and appropriate.

November 11, 1953
Veterans' Day. Alexander [work] went well, took a big step forward, I think. Walter explained how it is possible to contract rather than lengthen the arms and legs. I find such explanations very helpful.

November 18, 1953
I bought Paul Klee's *Pedagogical Sketchbook*.[86] Looking through it gave me the idea of using different sized arrows to diagram and to help visualize the Alexandrian directions. This might help to eliminate the almost irresistible tendency to try-and-feel-oneself-into-doing the directions or guiding orders, i.e., the neck to be free, the head to go forward and up, the torso to lengthen and the back to go back and widen. In visualizing the arrows, you "see" the direction of the energy and, perhaps, the magnitude of the energy required: the head as a more or less curved arrow pointing forward and up; the neck as a small arrow pointing back and up; the lengthening and widening back as two large double-headed arrows in the form of a cross; and finally the biggest and longest arrow pointing upward from the ankles into and through the torso to symbolize the lengthening of the stature.

To become conscious or aware of one's head! This is a difficulty. Ordinarily we are not kinesthetically aware of our heads, not to speak of other parts of the body. If we take the time, it is fairly easy to develop a kind of piecemeal awareness of the body, this part, then that part, etc. Much more difficult is to develop an awareness of the whole body-self in all its immediacy. More specifically, we want to attain an overall awareness of the whole body-self going UP! An anti-gravity awareness, if you like, while retaining your sense of terra firma, the ground you stand, sit or lie on.

When you do the wrong thing, the tendency is to then try and do the right thing. This is a false step. What you want is first to STOP! (inhibition); secondly, remember the guiding orders which then, thirdly, carry over into doing the thing you want to do. For example, if I decide to sit down, instead of acting at once (impulsively), and assuming I don't want to sit down the way I've always sat down (mechanicalness), I STOP! then direct my neck to be free, my head to go forward and up, my back to lengthen and move back to widen as I then, and only then, allow myself to sit down. And my attention remains on the process, the means-whereby, not the chair. This is your conscious control or, as John Dewey called it, "thinking-in-activity."

November 19, 1953

Walter Carrington said that, for the arms, energy should be directed along the back of the arm, not the front of the arm, thereby activating the extensor muscles, not the flexors. This is especially important in *teaching*. Directing energy so along the arms tends to bring the back into play: the strength and power of the back flows through the extensor muscles of the shoulders and the arms.

November 20, 1953

All this week Alexander work has gone well. Walter even mentioned it today. If I can continue like this, with no great sluggish periods, I will make progress and maybe begin using my hands on the other students. It is first and last a problem of fully realizing the primacy of *inhibition*: without this no changes can take place. It is also a matter of realizing how our old habits, however wrong or misguided, acquire the status of beliefs. We believe in our habits, and we feel secure in them. So we confront a complex of habit, belief and security resistant to inhibition and change.

———◦———

In January of 1954, I returned for a four months visit to America. I had been renting my house in South Salem, New York, but my tenants had moved. It was necessary to find other tenants and to do some upkeep work on the house, mostly painting the exterior. Besides this, I was hungry to see America again after three years in England.

June 1, 1954

I've been back in class for three weeks now. The work is going well. I think the four months in America was more beneficial than harmful. As William James[87] said, one learns to swim in winter and skate in summer.

Walter put my hands on the back of a chair today for the first time! The past week or so I've felt so different. I don't feel fat and sluggish!

June 14, 1954

This morning I took twenty of my paintings and hung them in The Writers and Artists Club, at 33 Haymarket, Piccadilly. The light is poor, the wall space small and broken up, a poor place to have an exhibition, but better than nothing for my first one-man show.

June 15, 1954

Thinking of the back now: thought today how seldom, if ever, one thinks of his or her back moving, in movement, like when the back lengthens and moves back to widen. Also, when we need to exert strength, we usually think of getting it from our arms or legs; whereas the source of the body is the *back*! I realize this fully now.

June 18, 1954

Walter C. made the following comments in class, which I put down in the order I remember them and not quoting directly: It's difficult to separate or sort out the difference between thinking of doing and doing… Children tend to learn the Technique quite readily because their sensory systems are generally more reliable than those of adults… Inhibition is the key, the foundation, of the Alexander Technique. Inhibition becomes progressively easier to apply in one's daily life as the use of the self improves. It is much easier to inhibit the impulse to do something when the neck is free, the head going forward and up, and the back lengthening and widening. (Walter gives us in that last sentence the operative reason why the Alexander Technique is so effective in changing, for example, one's negative habits, like smoking too much, drinking too much, losing temper, etc.) The first touch of the hands on the "pupil" is important. If it is not "right," then you must take your hands off and begin again.

June 21, 1954

Awareness of the whole self acting as a whole is to be achieved. Today I tried to become totally aware of myself, from the tips of my toes to the top of my head; then I tried to maintain this overall awareness in getting up out of a chair. I wasn't very successful. My attention was drawn to my legs, or my back, or my arms, always losing sight, even if momentarily, of the whole.

June 22, 1954

After breakfast I practised placing my hands on the back of a chair and was aware of my back widening. And as I thought about allowing my shoulders to widen or move away from each other, my ribcage expanded deeply bringing a deep breath into my lungs.

July 2, 1954

Yesterday Stewart Law and I had dinner with Walter and Dilys Carrington at their home. I was a little nervous but the more I thought about my *direction* the less nervous I was! Dilys is an attractive, sweet person. The dinner was delicious, and the few hours we were there were most enjoyable. Stewart had picked me up in his jeep, and as we were driving home he said he thought I'd been coming along especially well in the class during the last fortnight or so and he wondered if I was aware of it. I said I was and that I was pleased that he noticed it. He said: "I think you've come along as far in a fortnight as the rest of us have in the last four months." This was indeed satisfying to hear. Unquestionably, I have reached a new certainty and confidence in myself. Walter said to us the other day that one's "attitude of mind" is as fully important in this work as it is in life. He said that Alexander stressed its importance in his first book, *Man's Supreme Inheritance*. Walter added: "Of course, it's like the hen and the egg question." I remembered what Alexander had said to me during a lesson: "Life is a matter of conscious control and confidence."

July 5, 1954

A few days ago, in class, Peter S. said I was trying to help him take me forward and backward in the chair and, in consequence, shortening my stature. He said if I stop trying to help him and pay attention to my forward-and-up direction, I won't pull myself down.

Over the weekend I rewrote, expanded, and typed my notes to date in my journal on the Alexander Technique. I began to see the shape of a book consisting of my diary of lessons with Alexander and these notes.

I'm becoming aware of the use of the hands. Has there ever been a book called *The Use and Physiology of the Hand*? How absurdly little we know about ourselves and what we are capable of.

July 7, 1954

I asked Tony Spawforth during lunch yesterday when he thought I could start using my hands on the other students. He said, "When you are able to direct your orders." I said, "What do you mean by that?" He said, "When you know that your head is going forward and up, back widening, etc., in response to your [guiding] orders." With some surprise, I said, "I already know when I do or I don't respond to my inner directions." Tony replied that maybe I should ask Walter if I might begin using my hands. I said I would not—at least not for the time being.

I begin to see that one must go *forward and up* with one's entire being. Peggy Nixson (now Williams) said: "One must go up from the soles of one's feet, everything goes up!"

July 8, 1954

I was sleepy most of the day, feeling slightly hung over from the party last night. Walter told Liza to do some work on the other students. She worked on me and Walter came to help. He found my arms heavy and locked in the shoulders. Liza remarked how free my hands were. Walter said they were more collapsed than free. This struck me because lately I've become more aware of how I use my hands. I was also "down in the hips." I realized this but could do nothing, it seemed, to undo myself; probably making it worse by trying to do something about it. Walter said I must pay more attention to this habit of collapsing, especially in the lower back. He showed Liza how my back was sunk forwards. I asked: "Is this a result of collapsing or doing something?" He replied: "Collapsing!" He said his mother had a pronounced collapsed condition. He then said he had never seen (in respect to me) such a wide variation in the working of a back: when my back wasn't working it was terrible; but when it worked, it "worked like one o'clock!"

Both today and yesterday I felt truly at war with myself. I was pulling myself down and at the same time fighting against it. But suddenly in the last half hour of class today I came alive, light and going up! What a wonderful change. The contrast is remarkable. The opposite of a collapsed state is a state of expanding lightness and readiness. *I must not allow myself to collapse*.

July 13, 1954

Walter said that I'm tending to tighten my legs at the knees. I'm sure that doing this prevents my back from going back and widening. Liza said she thinks "visual attentiveness" is important for conscious control. I'm sure it is! Seeing objects clearly, within their surroundings, goes hand-in-hand with expanding awareness and conscious control. The opposite is staring, dreamy-eyed mind-wandering!

July 14, 1954
Peter S. said to me today: "Your head should go much farther forward than that." So this has been one of my difficulties during the past week: I have not really been directing my head forward. I've been thinking of the words but not fully releasing and directing the necessary energy. If the head is not truly going forward and up, the back cannot truly lengthen and widen.

July 16, 1954
In sitting down, Peter S. said I wasn't sufficiently letting my knees go forward. When you release the knees forward, the back will stay back and up, because the pelvis cannot tip forward and pull the lower back in. My arms and shoulders become more free. I tend to overlook the direction "to allow the ribs to contract," which Alexander always emphasized in his lessons to me.

July 17, 1954
I was reading the big scrapbook at Ashley Place and was surprised by the number of very well-known persons who have "endorsed" Alexander's work and which yet remains relatively unknown to the world, excepting perhaps in certain circles in London, New York, Boston, and Johannesburg. I was even more surprised to discover the name of one of my old professors at the New School for Social Research in New York City, Horace M. Kallen. I took several courses in philosophy with him and read his two-volume work *Art and Freedom*.[88] When I read his name in the scrapbook, I at once remembered how impressed I had been by his physical uprightness, his poise and bearing. He used to sit at his desk with his back well back against the back of his chair, the chair itself tilted backwards on its two back legs, his head seeming to spring up and turn so easily from side to side as he surveyed the class. There were also the names of James Harvey Robinson, the historian,[89] and V. F. Calverton, the sociologist,[90] both of whom taught at the New School.

July 19, 1954
The Alexander work goes well. I am realizing more fully the experience of my head going forward and up and neck tending to go back and up. The top

of the head becomes slightly inclined downwards from back to front (the degree of this "incline" will of course vary from one person to another), and one experiences a *pull* upwards, seemingly exerted by the head.

It is important to think of not doing the wrong thing rather than trying to do the right thing. To do so stops you from trying to do what you think is right and also from trying to be right. To try to stop yourself from end-gaining and, at the same time, ignore the means-whereby is also end-gaining.

It is important to clearly see that *use* and *functioning* are related: they are in direct correspondence. For example, as my *use* has changed and improved over the last several years, I no longer get depressed as I so frequently used to; I have much more energy and far, far more confidence in myself. My old back pains have stopped entirely, and I breathe more deeply and easily. These are the more obvious correspondences in my case.

July 22, 1954

I worked with several students after class today, putting my hands on Small Bill, and instantly realized that "teaching" is no simple, one-way, unilateral affair. You must be receptive as well as perceptive, and unless you, as "teacher," are working on yourself, you will convey almost nothing of value to your "pupil." I can hear John Dewey saying: this is more than an interaction, it is a transaction.

As Walter C. took me from sitting to standing today, I started to fall backwards, just as if something was pulling me back and down. Walter immediately said: "You're *collapsing* a little." I had felt this "pull" back-and-down before today, but I didn't recognize it as collapsing. If someone had asked me about it, I would have had to say I was off-balance.

A few days ago I met two Alexander teachers from New York, Judy Leibowitz[91] and Debby Frank,[92] here to have some lessons with Alexander. With them is a friend, singer, and Alexander student, Gladys Lea. They came over and had dinner with us last night. Debby is the daughter of Waldo Frank, the writer,[93] and Alma Frank, an Alexander teacher well known in Alexander circles for her study of infant development.[94] We all had a good time. Tomorrow they want to visit Dr. Wilfred Barlow[95] and his wife, Marjory; and I've decided to go with them.

July 24, 1954

At the Barlows. Dr. Barlow showed us some photographs of pupils taken before and after having lessons in the Technique. Some truly amazing changes were revealed in the photos. He said some of the pupils experienced striking personality changes. Dr. Barlow takes electromyographic readings of muscles under varying conditions of tension and conscious direction. The "graphs" show clearly the electro-muscular changes that take place when applying conscious direction and control. He takes X-rays of the spine in the neck and back that show a variety of forms of misuse.

Barlow emphasized that the above sort of work is only an adjunct to the teaching of the Technique. Mrs. Barlow said to me that she thinks Dr. Barlow's place in the work is to persuade the medical profession. They also believe that such records can be an added stimulus to pupils to work on themselves.

July 30, 1954

Last day at Ashley Place until September 13. My back went well back today, but I felt decidedly shortened, almost as if I were doubled up or leaning forward. Yet, *I knew this feeling was false.* Proof again of Alexander's contention that our feelings are unreliable. I decided to ignore this feeling that felt wrong and not to do anything that would make me feel right to myself.

Tomorrow Gita and I and some friends go to Rye for the three-day bank holiday. We hope for good weather. Margot and Arthur Nethercot were here for dinner. Margot is a cousin of Gita, and Arthur a professor of English literature at Northwestern University (my Alma Mater). Arthur is working on a book[96] on George Bernard Shaw and was most interested to hear of his relationship with Alexander.

August 2, 1954

We are back from a weekend in Rye. We had a wonderful time. Stayed at The Mermaid Inn, built in the year 1420. Henry James lived in Rye for a time.[97] The weather was very good, especially today. We swam at the beach on Sunday, played tennis today and lay in the sun.

August 5, 1954

The weather is extremely enervating. Did some painting this afternoon. Yesterday and the day before, I helped Elisabeth Bergner (the actress and close friend of Gita's stepmother) hang some paintings in her flat. She is a charming person.

Reread my journal of 1951–52. I must forge ahead with my painting, also my reading for my Alexander book. Do today what you plan to do!

August 20, 1954

I've begun separate journals for painting and for the Alexander Technique where I shall put down my notes and thoughts. I shall keep a third journal for comments on general activities. This is better, I think, than mixing every-thing up as I have so far. And this will help to focus my thinking on my principal activities, Alexander work and painting.

Liza Lechstein had dinner with us this evening. Had an interesting time.

Reading Giedion's *Space, Time, and Architecture* and find that one of his principal theses is the separation of thought and feeling in the individual and the need for their integration.[98] He says we have training in thinking but none in feeling. This shows a Deweyian influence, and it was F. M. Alexander who awakened Dewey to the fact of our unreliable feelings or sensory appreciation.

September 28, 1954
Yesterday, which began the third week of the new term—almost a month into my second year in the training course—I used my hands on other stu-dents for the first time. Walter C. had indicated to me on Friday that I was now ready to do so. Naturally, I am elated that this point has been reached.

Got a letter yesterday from Gladys Lea informing me that a Lee Firestone is in London on a Fulbright Scholarship to study acting and take lessons from Alexander. She called me on Saturday, and I will probably meet her this week at Ashley Place.

The painting goes along, have been doing some things with the palette knife: you get interesting textures quite as a matter of course: an example of how different results flow from different technical means.

September 19, 1954
Ray Bethers, from whom I've learned more than from anyone else on the art of painting, came over this evening and stayed for dinner. He said he was amazed by my "creativeness," liked what I was doing with the palette knife.

Stewart Law (from the training course) and I went to the Leicester Gal-leries to see an exhibit by Ronald Searle, the cartoonist, who takes Alexan-der lessons. We spent most of the time discussing the virtues of colonic irrigation. Searle's cartoons are wonderful, though not his excursions into serious painting.[99]

October 10, 1954
Here concludes the third volume of the journal I started in Ridgefield, Con-necticut, during the summer of 1948, right after my marriage to Morrell. How long ago that seems now. In those six years my life and myself have changed almost beyond recognition. I remember how Dr. Assia Abel, my Jungian analyst in New York, used to urge me to paint as a means of express-

ing myself. Well, I am painting, I am writing, and I'm well on my way to be a teacher of the Alexander Technique. As a teacher I will earn my livelihood and support Margrit [Gita] and the children we will have someday. I must work hard and produce. I will need all of my new faith and confidence.

October 11, 1954
A beautiful morning in London. As Alexander said to me one day: when London has good weather, there is none better anywhere. He was talking about the spring, but a good day is wonderful anytime here.

I shall go up a mile-a-minute today and make good use of my hands in class. I will also remember not to rely on feeling to tell me anything worthwhile about myself, especially as concerns the Technique.

October 17, 1954
A young English friend, Donald Southern, was with us for dinner. He is deeply in love with an American girl and worried about her fidelity. He is struggling to become a photographer, but has a sense of failure. I tried to "put him right" about these things and may have succeeded a little. I felt older and wiser. I realized how I've gained an inner strength, calmness and certainty of purpose. I tried to convey some of this to him. His problems, like mine, are mostly inside himself. I told him how the Alexander work has given me confidence and strength, where before there had been weakness and faint-heartedness. How little of the latter I know now!

October 18, 1954
The start of a new week, and it will be, I think, a good week for Alexander work. I think I've reached a fairly consistent standard of "constructive conscious control." I want to surround myself with paintings done by me and by others. In this way I communicate with the world and myself. Conscious control, like painting, is creative. What you create is a new use of yourself. This creation is a constant renewal: nothing static or fixed about it. The self, mind-and-body, is creating-and-being-created, all at the same time.

Like a painting the live body has a balance of forces not necessarily in equilibrium. In both it is a "tension" of relations between elements or parts in co-ordination or communication. Optimum communication or co-ordination in a painting or in the body-self depends on maximum awareness. The same is true of conversation as an art.

October 28, 1954
Tomorrow morning Erica Brausen (Hanover Gallery) comes to see my re-

cent paintings. I submitted two to the London Group exhibition. They were rejected. Surprisingly, instead of being depressed by this, I felt annoyance.

For the last ten nights before going to bed I've written a page or more in my Alexander journal and this has turned me to rereading Bentley[100] and Dewey. Both these activities, I notice, make me more awake and alert, helping my practical work in the training course.

November 7, 1954
I read in the *Sunday Times* Alan Moorehead's account of Winston Churchill's life. He did miserably in school until he was sent to Sandhurst, a military academy, at age 17. In that year, 1892, he developed his great interest, enthusiasm and love for life. Things that had been difficult for him now were easy. I noted the similarity between his and my own experience when I was about 16 (described in the first part of this book). Maybe it is a part of the normal adolescent experience. However, as the reader knows, I associated my "awakening" with the dramatic improvement in my posture produced by my wearing the torso-cast and doing the prescribed exercises that helped me maintain at least some degree of the new "straightness" in my torso. Except for a reading between the lines, there is no hint in Moorehead's article that anything like this happened to Churchill. However, his move from Harrow to the Sandhurst military academy might well have brought a change in his habitual posture, reducing an early tendency to collapse, which I infer from a description I read elsewhere, that Churchill at age 25 walked with a pronounced "forward stoop," which anybody can today observe he still has.

November 10, 1954
About every evening I also work on my autobiographical "novel" with so far 144 pages of script on the long foolscap sheets. Effortlessly, or almost so, I plunge into the past and reconstruct events. Things I don't remember at first tend to come flooding back as I persist in the focusing of my mind's eye on a particular period or time. Lately I've been working on a dialogue on the art of conversation, and my pen fairly flows along. When I put myself into the immediacy of the event, I don't have to stop and wonder what comes next: it just comes.

November 16, 1954
Several weeks ago I had letters from Judy Leibowitz and Gladys Lea. About her lessons with Alexander, Judy writes: "That Alexander is a great man! ...he sure can give you a sensory experience that is unequalled. I've come home with much clearer concepts and that helps my teaching." Gladys Lea,

who teaches singing, writes: "We have just begun working this week and feel very much benefited by our work with F. M. A.... There isn't anyone with his power and I find it a great privilege to know him. The connotations of the idea are infinite!"

I wrote them a joint letter today in which, among other things, I expressed some thoughts about training courses:

"Walter told me I was ready to begin using my hands on the other students. This was good news... So I've joined a group of four students, including myself, permitted to use their hands. Time is one of the most important factors in this work, as you know, and a maxim of the training course might be, 'If in doubt, take more time,' which applies to one's teaching too. I think a chief difficulty one faces in a training course, true of any training course, is that, by definition, a training course will in *practice* tend towards end-gaining practices, such as being too careful, trying-to-be-right, etc. But if the students develop a lucid appreciation of the importance of inhibition in their practical work, and if a congenial atmosphere surrounds the group, I think this difficulty can be greatly minimized."

"Meanwhile the painting also goes quite well. I must say I find it an excellent accompaniment to the work at Ashley Place... It's a rather curious fact that my 'style' changed quite radically about the time I began using my hands in the training course."

November 17, 1954
Erica Brausen visited and liked my recent paintings and said she will later choose three for a mixed exhibition. Her special criticism was that my whites are generally too white and my blacks too black. I must learn to build up color. She wanted to know how I begin a painting.

November 19, 1954
More and more I realize that if I do not interfere with myself in whatever I do, all will come out as I want it to. And I mean interference in painting and in writing, as well as interference in the *use* of myself which underlies everything. To doubt oneself is an interference like tensing the neck is an interference. These two interferences feed on each other and lead to inaction and depression.

I gave an Alexander "turn" to a friend last night. He said he envied me because it seemed to him I have a calmness of mind that strikes him as unusual. He is the third person who has said something like this within the past year.

November 24, 1954
I received a note from the photographer John Roder. He saw my one-man show at the Writers and Artists Club and said he would like to photograph me for an article he's doing for a photography magazine. Of course, I said yes.

I begin to think I can write fairly well, unevenly, but well. I'm gradually realizing my wishes, my life-long wishes.

Went to the Diaghilev exhibition at Forbes House during lunch and was very moved by it, especially the music from his ballets.[101] The figures in the photos and drawings sprang to life before my eyes.

December 13, 1954
I had a superb day in Alexander class despite having a bad cold. Said "good-bye" to Elmer Tolsted, a cellist and teacher of mathematics at Pomona College in California, here having Alexander lessons. He said he will send me pupils when I begin teaching in America.

December 16, 1954
Rather depressed. Erica Brausen called me yesterday to say she would like to hang three pictures in a joint exhibition during February. So today I took them to her gallery and was shocked to see my greys turn muddy and dead in the neon light of the gallery. Impossible to hang them! The joy of yesterday no more. Too much raw umber I think.

December 22, 1954
We arrived in Zurich for the holidays three days ago. I am in a comfortable room a few hundred yards down the road from the home of Margrit's parents in Zollikon. The two days before we left London were horrible. I was in the depths of a depression I haven't known for many, many months, and even broke down a couple of times, but only for a minute or two. The fiasco with my paintings did it, of course. How different my feelings would have been had they been acceptable. It was a ghastly two days, but after we got a good start on our trip I was alright. The Channel crossing was in perfect weather. We spent the first night in Rheims and saw the cathedral in the morning sunlight, a magnificent structure, floating like a giant bird in the sky.

January 22, 1955
Back in London after driving through dense fog all the way from Dover. From Zurich, we spent successive nights in Bad Nauheim, Amsterdam, The Hague and Ghent. We visited the State and the Municipal museums in Amsterdam and the Gemeede Museum in The Hague. This last was a disap-

pointment, except for the Mondrian[102] and Kuniyoshi[103] exhibits, an interesting contrast.

Did a dozen drawings in ink and crayon.

January 24, 1955
First day of the new term at Ashley Place. Walter C. has introduced, provisionally, a new procedure. He will devote the afternoon sessions to working with several students on using their hands.

Walter asked me to observe Liza's neck as she put her hands on Stewart. He showed me the difference in the look and feel of the neck when the head is pulled back and the neck is not completely free, and when the head is tilted back and the neck *is* free. In the first instance there was a slight bulging or swelling of the muscles at the base and back of the neck, hardly noticeable unless one looked closely.

We discussed the lengthening of the back or torso. The back cannot lengthen if there is any "pull" or contraction of the muscles of the stomach, chest or throat-neck. It is so easy to do this and not be aware of doing it. Obviously, the entire torso (front, back and sides) wants to be lengthening, going up!

January 26, 1955
Some points covered in class today:

The teacher gets nowhere by *pulling*! Instead of releasing or yielding or undoing, the pupil will resist.

While going on with his or her directions, the first essential step for the teacher is to see that the pupil is inhibiting, is applying his powers of inhibition to the best of his or her ability at this stage.

When lying on the table, to direct the knees upward helps prevent contracting the thigh and calf muscles. And lengthening the hand from the wrist and slightly raising the hand, palm facing down, helps prevent contracting the flexor muscles of the forearm.

To a student who was working on another, Walter said: "Don't take all night to do it." He said if one hesitates too much one becomes too careful. And confidence everywhere diminishes.

February 4, 1955
Reading C. S. Sherrington's *Man on His Nature*, a fascinating book, thought-provoking.[104] What an incredible mechanism the eye is!

I gave Daisy, our landlady, an Alexander "turn" today. Her neck is in bad shape, shortened and pulled forward and down; and her upper back badly humped. At this stage I merely want to give her the idea that she doesn't have to pull herself down in the way she does, that she can allow herself to come up in front and lengthen her stature. As she grasps the idea of inhibiting, I will give her the guiding orders. She enjoys the "treatment," as she calls it, finds it restful and relieving to her back.

I seem to be changing from a left-hander to a right-hander. Some months ago I gradually switched from drawing with my left to drawing with my right hand. With the latter I felt less "fixed," more free. Then, a week or so ago, I experimented with writing in my journal with my right hand. Now I no longer feel like using my left hand.

February 16, 1955
Walter stressed the importance of not over-using the hands on a pupil: the teacher wants to pause or even stop occasionally to check his or her own use, freeing the hands, etc. This is a continuous process, of course; the point being to work toward a minimal use of the hands as you develop and improve your own conscious direction and control in teaching. He said that otherwise you tend to interfere with the pupil's own responsibility and initiative in the directing process. Alexander's use of his hands was, as I remember, minimal; his touch was gentle but, at the same time, definite and firm. The teacher will also want to adjust his or her manner of working to the changing state and need of the pupil.

February 17, 1955
Peggy Nixson (now Williams) suggested to Walter that I put my hands on her. I sat her in the chair and was amazed at how light she was, as if she weighed nothing at all. Walter said my back was widening and lengthening well but that my arms and hands had little direction in them. He then placed his hands on my *neck* in a way that illustrated what he meant. Immediately, I observed the difference between the use of my hands and arms without direction and their use with direction. The lesson here is this: the *whole entire self wants direction!*

February 18, 1955
As I sat in my chair in class this morning, I was thinking of the pupil as an *extension* of the teacher: if the teacher is expanding (lengthening and widening) and going up in all his other parts when he or she puts his or her hands on the pupil, then, willy-nilly, the pupil will expand and go up too. As Alexander said to me in a lesson on October 17, 1951: "Why, Mr. Binkley, when I am teaching you, as I do now, I am able to convey to you what I want

to convey, because as I touch you and guide you with my hands in carrying out my instructions, I, myself, am going up! up! up!"

To understand the concept of DIRECTION and to appreciate its practical importance is a vital necessity for the Alexander pupil, I believe. Of course, the difficulty is that until you have become more or less familiar with experiencing *direction in yourself*, it's almost impossible to have a right conception of it.

It is good to remember that you are a man or a woman in the full biological-evolutionary sense; that you are not merely a part of nature, you *are* nature. When you are awake, alert and aware of yourself in the full Alexandrian sense, you are nature being conscious of herself. When you speak, nature is speaking.

March 8, 1955
I gave a "turn" to Helen Hoadley today, who is asthmatic. I worked on her back and shoulders with a few light touches to her neck and head. Placing my hand on her sternum area seemed to help her breathing, giving it a longer, more normal, rhythm. Her shoulders are tight and narrowed. She does not let go of her arms. When I told her she was holding on to them, she said she thought she was doing just the opposite. Her lower back is extremely lordotic. She gets "support" from a tight corset she has worn for 20 years. Her neck is so shortened and pulled forward that it seems to disappear at the back. Her flesh feels cold, moist, toneless and flabby (writing 25 years later I would have said she is decidedly hypoascorbemic, that is, unknowingly suffering from a deficiency of ascorbic acid, or vitamin C). After the "turn," she said: "I think you freed me a little."

In the late afternoon I gave a "turn" to Elisabeth Bergner. Afterwards she told me a funny story about Paul Czinner, her husband, and she laughed until tears came to her eyes. I wondered if this were partly an emotional release in reaction to the Alexander work. She readily responded to my hands and was most appreciative in her comments.

March 10, 1955
I recently discovered in myself these two connections: I cannot consistently release or let go of my knees in letting them go forward if I'm tensing or holding-on in my toes, feet and ankles; and, secondly, if I really pay attention and allow my rib-cage to contract optimally, then my lower back moves back of itself, as it were.

March 15, 1955
Walter worked with me today. He says my chief difficulty now is too much tension! He said I'm doing too much from my shoulders, not enough from my back. I must not raise the shoulders. He had me work on Small Bill, with good results.

Late in the afternoon I gave Helen H. her third "turn." I spent a little more time than before in freeing her neck and directing her head forward and up. I gave her the verbal guiding orders or directions, including "allow the ribs to contract." She asked what this meant. I explained by holding my arm outstretched and "allowing it to drop." I think this would have been more effective if I had used *her* arm. After the "turn" she said she didn't want to flatter me but she thought the "treatment" was very good. I told her she was a good pupil because she was attentive and that she would make good progress if we keep at it for a time.

March 17, 1955
I have definitely progressed in the use of myself this past week or so. Have reached a new, higher standard. No doubt my giving "turns" to family and friends has helped; also, the "mirror work" I've done lately at Ashley Place. I am more sure about what I am doing and not doing.

I gave Daisy another "turn." She shows definite signs already of the benefits. She is gayer and less nervous. Her back is much improved, the hump greatly reduced, and she says she "feels better."

March 25, 1955
After class this afternoon I had tea with Anna H. and Tony S. Then I went back to Ashley Place and worked for half an hour in front of the mirror. I noticed myself tending to raise and push out my chest when I was thinking about trying to lengthen my stature. When I stopped trying and simply allowed my thinking to direct the energy, I could clearly see that I was lengthening without raising my chest.

April 3, 1955
I'm "going up" beautifully. I'm aware of an "inner force" taking me up out of my feet. I've reached a higher standard of *use* and *sensory appreciation*.

April 27, 1955
Third day of work at Ashley Place after the spring holidays. And each day I've done work with my hands under Walter's guidance, twice on Stewart L. and today on Jean Macklin, a new student from America, though she's Eng-

lish. For the first time I took someone out of a chair. Worked with some of the students for an hour and a half after class. Liza and I gave Small Bill a long turn in the chair and on the table.

April 29, 1955
Making good progress this week. On Friday Walter asked me to help him give Anna H. a turn on the table. He announced a new policy for the training course: a student will pay for the minimum three years, but if he needs more time to become qualified, he has an option of a fourth year. Beyond the fourth year, a new financial arrangement must be made. But if a student hasn't qualified at the end of four years, it isn't likely he ever will. He said a student really ought to qualify in three years.

May 8, 1955
I use my hands every day now in class. Peter Scott said aloud in class that I was becoming a "joy to work on." And Walter responded, "He is! He is!"

For a few days now I've been modelling in clay, which I get from the Chelsea Pottery just two blocks away on the other side of the King's Road. After firing in the kiln it becomes dull brick red.

June 16, 1955
Five weeks since last entry and starting work in terra cotta. I've done ten pieces, including an almost life-size head of Alexander, from memory and photographs in the *New Leader* magazine. When I'm working the clay, I try to handle it with *direction*, as in Alexander teaching.

Margrit and I have set August 18 for our wedding day. Mother is coming over and so are Margrit's parents.

June 30, 1955
Alexander work goes well but could be better. Partly one's inner attitude—so important. I must learn to overcome any signs of timidity in class—if I feel that I am going well enough to use my hands, I should jolly well use them.

July 3, 1955
Played two sets of tennis in the morning, painted several of my small terra cotta pieces, and typed a few more pages of my "book."

Patricia and Peter, friends of ours, came for dinner and to spend the night. I gave them both a turn. During Peter's turn, he suddenly said that he could see more clearly.

Only four weeks left in the term at Ashley Place.

August 18, 1955
Our wedding day!

November 17, 1955
I wrote a letter to Judy Leibowitz which said in part:
"As I am sure you have heard, the principal event on this side of the ocean in our work was the death of F. M. Alexander on October 10. He died quietly about 11 o'clock on a Monday morning. As it happened, that very day I came down with the flu and was confined to bed for five days. Tuesday morning I was in bed reading *The Times* and did something I've never done before, scanned the obituary columns and there saw his name. It was quite a shock as you may imagine. He had had a mild heart attack two weeks previously and was recovering so well that we all expected his imminent return to work at Ashley Place. A nurse who was with him at the time said he was in good spirits and sitting up in bed when he suddenly lay back on his pillow and died. He was cremated on Thursday."

December 31, 1955
Joanna Claudia Elizabeth was born at 2:25 a.m.

February 20, 1955
Walter showed Tony Spawforth how he should go up or lengthen while teaching. And you don't move the pupil just with hands and arms but with your whole body. It was clear from Walter's demonstration that the pupil becomes an *extension* of the teacher, as I expressed it in my journal. Walter also instructed Tony to not put his hands on the pupil with the intention of doing something to him but rather with the intention of doing something with *himself*. In short, don't end-gain in your teaching!

February 21, 1956
In demonstrating this morning, Walter used the words "springing" and "upward impulse." With your head going forward and up and your back lengthening and widening, you initiate a gradual process of "building up" the "upward impulse."
Many, if not most, people, Walter said, habitually tense their thighs, abdomen and pectoral muscles, thereby pulling down in front and so preventing the lengthening and widening of the back. Most of the extensor muscles contribute to counteracting gravity.

February 22, 1956

Walter said that Alexander considered *inhibition* to be the first step in any activity. I asked if inhibition also applied during the process of the act or activity. He agreed that it did. I asked if it was useful for the teacher to think of his or her pupil as an extension of himself or herself. He agreed that it was. In answer to a question from Pat Peacock, he said it was demonstrable that the right thing will *not* take care of itself.

Discussing collapsed shoulders, Walter said it was better to err on the side of stiffening than collapsing; better to stiffen the shoulders a little than let them collapse. Usually, he said, it is easier to cope with a person who is generally too tense than one who is generally collapsed. How well I know this!

March 1, 1956

The past two days not too good at Ashley Place, so I've gone back to fundamentals, doing some mirror work, and putting my hands on the back of a chair, etc. A colleague in class asked me how one can feel depressed or be in a bad mood and yet be going well Alexanderwise. I answered, "Sensory appreciation!" At such times one is less liable to try to do, to try and feel, or to concentrate.

March 7, 1956

According to Walter, Alexander used to teach as many as 18 pupils per day in New York during the years (1916-1924) of his six-month long visits there. In London the rest of the year, he treated himself to a less demanding schedule.

Walter and Peggy together gave me a turn today. Walter moved my head back and forth and said I was lifting my chest. He told Peggy to put a hand on my chest and the other on my back. After this I felt freer in my hips.

Constance Tracey is definitely improving. Walter helped her put her hands on Small Bill. He said her back had greatly improved in the past two months.

Jean Macklin has some difficulty with her lower back. She tends to pull herself down in front and gets a heaviness under her jaw in consequence, among other things.

I gave table turns to Stewart Law, Edward Gellatly and Ted Peacock. Standing behind the head, I experimented with an upward "pull" on the thoracic cage with, I think, good results: it helped the lengthening and released the rib-cage. Ted's chief problem at present is collapsed shoulders making his arms very heavy. When Edward got off the table, he said he felt quite different.

I gave chair turns to Anna Haddon, Dorothy Corfe, Tony S., Edward, and Ted.

March 8, 1956
Tony came over last night and we took turns reading aloud the first few pages of *Constructive Conscious Control of the Individual.* And this morning I gave chair turns to Kirk Rengstorff, who is making excellent progress, in my opinion, to Tony and to Small Bill. Bill tends to pull or drop his neck forward. Tony does too. In consequence, they both, in their past years, developed rounded or humped upper backs.

My special problems at this time, things I want to be especially aware of, are undue tension in my legs and feet, and a tendency to unduly raise my chest, which prevents proper widening of the back.

March 12, 1956
I gave Kirk a turn this morning, and he asked to watch him while "trying to lengthen and widen" his back. I did so and saw right away that his "lengthening" was at the expense of the widening of his back which was, in fact, *narrowing.* He said he had been making the mistake of thinking of lengthening from the "base of his trunk," whereas Walter had told him to think of lengthening from the ankles.

March 14, 1956
This morning I noticed that Ted P., like Kirk R., tends to lengthen at the expense of widening his back. Maybe this is a special problem for persons with long backs. Both Kirk and Ted are tall with long backs, especially Kirk.

As for myself, I must give more thought to *my* back. I tend to pull my lower back *in* while teaching, or doing anything else for that matter. I simply have to *stop* this pulling-in of my lower back. It will help if I *stop* the needless tightening of my buttocks and leave them alone.

March 23, 1956
Last day of class before our two-week Easter holiday.

About using the hands: it is important to also let the wrists and fingers lengthen as the whole arm lengthens. I've neglected this lately. Perhaps I've thought too much, or too directly, of my back. For I have noticed that when I maintain awareness of my hands, wrists and arms, especially in teaching, this helps my back to lengthen and widen.

As I review my work since the beginning of the term in January, I can't say I've made the progress I expected to.

April 17, 1956
I went to the AIA gallery[105] to pay the hanging fee for their new exhibition in which I have one painting and one small terra cotta sculpture, titled *Woman Sitting*, and found that the latter has been sold!

April 18, 1956
Walter said today that the only reason to move one's head is not to move any other part of the body. An interesting and enlightening remark. He gave me a turn while Peggy "took his back." A wonderful turn. I was doing well, really had the upward impulse. Walter took me smartly back and forth in the chair a half dozen times just lightly touching my neck. What I've got now in the past few days is the firmly realized experience of going up and widening—the springing, upward surging impulse!

May 3, 1956
About the whispered "ah:" the "ah" wants to be really an ah, except whispered. However, the breath is not just breathed out. It wants to be more energetic than that, though not forced. This is an error I've been making.

May 7, 1956
I'm rereading C. Judson Herrick's fascinating biography[106] of George E. Coghill—who wrote the introduction to Alexander's last book, *The Universal Constant in Living*—with new understanding. The human species seems to have lost the sensory appreciation of the "total pattern" (Coghill's term) of behavior. In recovering, through Alexander lessons, the "total pattern" itself and his sensory appreciation of it, modern man not only recaptures his birthright of this *universal constant* but also raises himself to a new plane of *constructive conscious control*.

July 12, 1956
Walter stressed the importance of freeing the neck. It is fundamental. If the neck is truly free, he said, you can "do" almost anything you like to lengthen. It is important for the wrists to be free and lengthening, otherwise the hands will be less sensitive, less intelligent.

Peggy said she finds it helpful not to think too carefully about what she is doing while teaching. I too have observed this. I think what is involved here is the refusal to concentrate in the ordinary way. Concentration, as

Alexander said, not only reduces awareness—it also builds up tension and interference.

July 19, 1956
Walter said the pupil should not try to feel what the teacher does with his or her hands, but rather should carry on with his own internal process of *ordering* and *directing*. In the Alexander work, our aim is to control the *reaction*, not the stimulus. He said Alexander wrote his second book, *Constructive Conscious Control of the Individual*, in a room in which a small child was playing most of the time.

Walter also made the following comments:

F. M. used to say that a good result can be obtained through any number of means, but the one means we want is the control of reaction. ... Alexander had hoped to get Julian Huxley's support for the Technique.[107] He gave a dinner at the Café Royal [c. 1938] for Aldous, Julian, J. E. R. McDonagh,[108] and Anthony Ludovici[109] and a few others, mainly for the purpose of winning over Julian. But in spite of his brother Aldous's enthusiasm, Julian remained unsympathetic. ... *Change* is the main thing. ... I've never known a pupil not to have "Alexander depressions" in the beginning stages. ... You can get a pupil going very nicely—lengthening, light on the feet, breathing well, and so on, and yet have achieved little in the way of *inhibition*.

June 25, 1956
Again, the importance of freeing the neck: you can't take the pupil's head forward and up, and you can't take the pupil's neck back, unless the neck is free! If the neck is not free, there is no way of getting a *connection*.

The above point came up while Walter was giving a turn to Ted Peacock. Small Bill said he hadn't been able to take Ted's neck back or to stop him from pulling his neck forward and down. Walter said that the teacher's ability to help free a pupil's neck depended on the teacher's own *use* and experience.

September 24, 1956
Teaching in class this first week of the new term is suddenly a new experience. I seem to have my whole back, indeed my whole self in my *hands*.

October 1, 1956
I've been thinking of a plan for a ballet based on the Alexander Technique. There is the teacher and his pupils. The pupils come on stage, awkward, clumsy movements heads pulled back, pulled down, exaggerated curvatures

in the back, stress and strain written all over their bodies and faces. Then the teacher comes dancing on the stage, light, graceful, leaping and bounding in the air. The teacher then darts about and amongst the stressed and awkward people. Suddenly he approaches one and guides him to a chair, touches his neck, head and torso with swift, deft movements of the hands. The pupil rises transformed from the chair, transfigured, and he too begins to dance with a look of astonishment on his face which turns to delight and ecstasy as he dances his solo. The others watch him with puzzled expressions—they cannot understand this transformation. So the teacher goes to another, and then another, of the pupils, each of whom springs up surprised and delighted. The pupils as dancers could be engaged in various daily-life activities, like sweeping a floor, washing clothes, typing a letter, eating a meal, and so on, both before and then after their transformation. The transition from bad to good use could be shown as a gradual happening.

October 3, 1956
I had a private lesson with Walter. I told him about the diary I kept of my lessons with Alexander and he wants to see it. About my progress in the training course, he said the only comment he had to make is that there is still a big difference between my back working well and my back working badly. He said I should now get as much experience as possible using my hands in class. Then soon he will start me helping him with several of his private pupils.

October 12, 1956
All last week I typed out my diary of lessons with Alexander and gave it to Walter to read. Today he said: "It's first rate!"

   Yesterday I was thinking of "going up" or lengthening in terms of imagining a point in space just above the top of my head. Then I extended this idea to include awareness of a sort of spatial envelope surrounding my body-self. This awareness seemed to counteract the sometimes irresistible tendency to try and *feel* the body-self going up. The idea of a "spatial envelope" helps to remind us that we exist and live in a medium that has mass, exerts pressure, offers resistance and effortlessly fills our lungs when we allow the rib cage to expand and contract.

October 15, 1956
I was thinking of Alexander's *inhibition* in connection with Korzybski's *delayed reaction*. The two terms mean only partly the same thing. Inhibition

means not only the stop or delay of reaction but also means the carrying over of the inhibitory idea into and *during* the action or reaction.

Up until Thursday of last week my teaching was going really well. But now, like today, I have little confidence in putting my hands on anyone. My arms, as Peggy noted today, seem to be collapsed. She said: "You seem to be entering a new era in your work. I hope it isn't going to be too terrible for you." That, at least, may be a more positive look at what, in my present dark mood, seems to be a relapse—I am even tempted to say, collapse!

October 17, 1956
I've nearly recovered from the "lifelessness" of the past few days. More than ever I realize the truth in the phrase, "the energy of thought," which Winifred Dussek says Alexander used in his book, *The Use of the Self*, though I don't recall it. What one must reach is a plane of active and consistent *direction*.

When I complained once to Alexander that I was conscious of excessively tensing my neck while eating and talking, he replied: "You are more than likely unduly relaxing, not tensing, your neck." I now see that he was right!

I think some people have to make more of an *effort* in this work. I am one of them, thanks to my old habit of generally collapsing.

October 18, 1956
Last night I began annotating my diary of lessons with Alexander with quotations from his four books, my idea being to complement what he said and did with what he wrote.

During class I gave Walter a turn while Peggy worked on me. Afterwards he made no critical remarks but seemed pleased and benefited. He did say not to work (use my hands on others) at any expense to myself. For example, Peggy noticed what she called a "twist" in my torso, but this was due simply to not placing my feet to my best mechanical advantage.

Today and also yesterday I again experienced my whole body-self going up! up! up!

I increasingly appreciate the significance of something Alexander emphasized, namely, having the *wish* or *desire* to go up! The *wish* helps to mobilize the energy required. It provides a kind of bridge between the thought of doing something and the doing of it.

October 19, 1956
Walter said to Edward G. that if the pupil is properly inhibiting and carrying out the guiding orders, then the "right" thing will tend to take care of itself;

and so the teacher need not insist on pointing out minor or local patterns of interference, such as stiffening the legs, which Edward tends to do. Otherwise, your pupil may try to concentrate on that or some other specific area and, in the process, neglect the primary head-and-neck-and-torso relationship.

Walter also said that, generally speaking, he is opposed to the use of mirrors by pupils, his main objection being that, again, there is just this danger of the pupil concentrating on "specifics."

He also remarked that "mental" pulling-down was just as serious, if not more so, than "physical" pulling down, though one cannot draw a sharp line between the two aspects. But pupils do tend to think that *pulling-down* is primarily a "physical" thing to be corrected by primarily "physical" means. It is expedient, therefore, to emphasize the "mental" side of pulling-down. Which is why confidence and a positive attitude are so important.

October 23, 1956
The Alexander school and our teachers have moved from Ashley Place to Bainbridge Street, just off New Oxford Street, and we had a party there last night.

Walter said he was worried about my "stability," the chief difficulty being my feet, ankles and knees. I definitely agree. Part of the trouble is that no one, excepting Walter himself, gives me a proper turn on the table—though Peggy helped a great deal today when she decided to pay attention to my feet and ankles.

Today is my birthday and tonight we are going to see a play, *A Likely Tale*, with Robert Morley and Margaret Rutherford.[110] Dinner afterwards.

November 2, 1956
This past week Walter was away in Guernsey, and all the training course students were offered a lesson by Margaret Goldie. I had my lesson today.

EPILOGUE

I was in the teachers' training course for four years. During that time Gita and I were married, Alexander died (October 10, 1955), and our two daughters, Joanna and Jessica, were born. The training course was led by Walter Carrington assisted by Peter Scott and, later, Peggy Williams. After Alexander's death, his staff of teachers and we students in the training course moved from Ashley Place to No. 5 Bainbridge Street.

In late 1956, because of an accident to his leg, Walter had to stop teaching for six weeks or so. Margaret Goldie kindly and generously offered to give us all private lessons in his absence. I continued these weekly lessons with her until shortly before our departure for America in November 1957. Earlier in 1956 Walter asked me to re-edit a manuscript called *Alexander and the Doctors*, consisting mainly of testimony taken at a trial in South Africa resulting from Alexander's suit for libel against the editors of a journal called *Manpower* (the defendants had to pay damages and costs).[111] This task consumed a good deal of my time and energy during my last year in London, but of course it was a task I wanted to do and I went at it with enthusiasm. I kept on with my art work in these years, exhibiting in half-a-dozen group shows and selling several items. I had a one-man show at the Writers and Artists Club.

In America my wife and I and baby daughters settled in my house in South Salem which I had rented during the years in London.

I taught in New York City for a few years, at first with Judy Leibowitz and then mostly on my own. In the 1960s my two sons, David and Mark, were born. In 1963, not being able to make ends meet at this time solely as an Alexander teacher, I took a high school teaching job offered me by a friend, pupil and neighbor, Elliot (Red) Noyes. He was the principal of the school. I taught Chemistry there (Brewster, New York) for four years and at two other schools for four years. During this time I gave Alexander lessons in New York City on Friday afternoons and Saturdays.

In the fall of 1971, after resigning as a high school teacher, I moved to Chicago resolved to henceforth teach the Alexander Technique full-time. My wife and four children joined me in 1973. We lived in my mother's home in Glencoe for a few years and then, in 1977, bought our own home just down the street. In 1975, accepting five of my regular pupils as trainees, I started a teachers' training course. We found permanent quarters at 116 S. Michigan Avenue, right across from the Chicago Art Institute, and called it the Chicago Center for the Alexander Technique. We were affiliated with the Society of Teachers of the Alexander Technique in London. I was also a member of the New York Center for the Alexander Technique. During these years in the '70s, I gave numerous lecture-demonstrations and made monthly teaching visits to Minneapolis, Milwaukee and Bloomington, Indiana, where I taught at the music school of Indiana University.

As I write these lines (in late October 1985) I am divorced and living and teaching in Paris, France, and making monthly visits to Geneva and Zurich. I moved here in November of 1981 to be with my then student, Micheline Valissant. She is now an Alexander teacher.

———◆———

That F. Matthias Alexander was a genius, those who knew and worked with him agree. His was a great achievement! But one has to think a little, to turn exactly what he did over in one's mind to fully savor the magnitude of his discoveries—a means of controlling human reaction from *within* and, inseparable from this, the primary control in the use of the self. A *conscious control*, Alexander also called it—a means of by-passing, as it were, the subconscious, the usual sort of acting-by-instinct. In process, it is a means also of better co-ordinating-integrating man's (yours and mine) triune brain (McLean[112]). In the process, again, you shed your fear, your "paranoia,"— all the negative things that tend to limit you, and thus, with your expanding self, expanding your love and acceptance of your fellow man. This is the moral effect, if you like, the spiritual effect of Alexander's work, of his gift to us.

Notes

For the preparation of these notes primary sources, where available, have been consulted—mainly at the British Library. We would like to express our gratitude to Maxwell Alexander, Marjory Barlow, Deborah Caplan, Walter Carrington, Bill Connington, Richard M. Gummere, Jr., Shoshana Kaminitz, Alison Macdonald, Mary Scott and Peggy Williams for information on much of the history of the Alexander Technique. Naturally, any faults and omissions are entirely our responsibility.

Ian MacFadyen

Jean M. O. Fischer

---

1   Ernest (Miller) Hemingway (1899-1961), U. S. novelist and short-story writer, awarded the Nobel Prize for Literature in 1954. He is famous for *A Farewell to Arms* (1929), *For Whom the Bell Tolls* (1940) and *The Old Man and the Sea* (1952). His life and his writings were characterised by masculine values and permanent adventurous rebellion. JMOF

2   Sherwood Anderson (1876-1941), U.S. novelist, essayist, poet, travel writer and newspaper editor. Anderson was both a modernist influenced by Gertrude Stein, and a naturalist and populist. His most famous novel is *Winesburg, Ohio* (1919), a series of related short stories about the pathos and tragedy of small-town American life. Anderson's many novels explore sexuality, mystical forces and social alienation. A selection of his letters was published in *Letters: selected and edited with an introduction and notes by Mumford Jones* (1953). IMCF

3   Aldous (Leonard) Huxley (1894-1963), English author and essayist, wrote, among other novels, *Those Barren Leaves* (1925), *Point Counter Point* (1928), *Brave New World* (1932), and described his hallucinogenic mescaline-induced experiences in *The Doors of Perception* (1954) and *Heaven and Hell* (1956). Huxley started having lessons with F. M. Alexander in November 1935 and had lessons as late as in 1960. The influence of the Alexander Technique in his writings is most notable in *Eyeless in Gaza* (1936) and *Ends and Means* (1937). Alexander's work is referred to in Huxley's essays "The Education of an Amphibian" (in *Adonis and the Alphabet*, 1956), "Human Potentialities" (in *The Humanist Frame*, 1961) and, implicitly, in his novel *Island* (1962). A life-long supporter of the Technique other writings on the Technique include a review of F. M. Alexander's *The Universal Constant in Living* (1942), and the foreword to Louise Morgan's *Inside Yourself* (1954). JMOF

4   Count Alfred (Habdank Skarbek) Korzybski (1879-1950), U. S. Polish-
born semanticist who came to the U. S. about 1915. Korzybski taught a
system of linguistics called "General Semantics" which rejects the Aristotelian structure of language with its "is" of identity and its limiting "either-
or" polarisations. Korzybski believed that people confuse words with the
things for which they stand, and that their behaviour is influenced, often
triggered, by words and word associations. He devised a number of exercises
to assist in liberating people from habitual responses to language. Korzybski
was President and Director of the Institute of General Semantics from 1938
to his death. His books include *Manhood of Humanity: The Science and Art
of Human Engineering* (1921), *Time-Binding: The General Theory* (1926) and
Science and Sanity: an Introduction to Non-Aristotelian Systems (1933), the
"fountainhead" and seminal text of General Semantics. (*See also* note 5)
IMCF

5   General Semantics studies the processes through which we learn, know and
communicate. It questions our habitual unconscious responses to language
and the automatic actions which result. It is a form of *re-education*. Korzybski:
"It turns out that in the structure of our languages, methods, 'habits of
thought,' orientations, etc., we preserve delusional psychopathological factors. These are in no way inevitable, as will be shown, but can be easily
eliminated by special training, therapeutic in effect, and consequently of
educational preventive value…" (p. ii). He adds that "the linguistic structural, semantic issues represent powerful and ever present environmental
factors, which constitute the most important components of our problems."
(p. ii and v.) General Semantics employs a number of techniques for increasing awareness of automatic responses in language use, thought processes and actions: mental QUOTES as a warning that words are only approxi-
mations; the use of ET CETERA, a reminder that a statement cannot say
everything about a subject; the mental HYPHEN which overcomes dichoto-
mous either-or thinking; the semantic INDEX which affixes a number and
specific information to an event, to prevent generalisation; the INTERCON-
NECTION of different subjects; the development of INTERNAL SILENCE; the
principle of NON-IDENTIFICATION: "Maps are not their territories; words are
not their facts." Binkley mentions the DELAY OF REACTION, a technique which
breaks automatic semantic connections; the delay corrects assumptions
about language and the world by the conscious intervention of a re-evalu-
ating process which re-checks incoming data and reactive impulses. This is
literally a "Stop and Think" initiative which allows a person to review
preconceptions, the present situation and future options, and determine an
appropriate response. The DELAY OF REACTION attempts to abolish the impul-
sive and habitual recognition of linguistic signals, and institute in their place
creative correspondences and conscious choice: Korzybski refers to this as
"the lengthening of nerves," making the point that the technique has an

actual physiological effect upon the brain. General Semantics is sometimes referred to as "neuro-semantics" or "neuro-linguistics." In *Science and Sanity* (1933) Korzybski lists scores of "projected" publications covering all aspects of the human sciences. IMCF

6   Pietr Demianovich Ouspensky (1878-1947), Russian mathematician, mystic and writer. Ouspensky is the most famous pupil of the Armenian spiritual charismatic teacher George Ivanovitch Gurdjieff (1866?-1949), although their relationship was problematic and they were colleagues for only brief periods of time. In *A New Model of the Universe* (written 1912-1929), Ouspensky theorizes that time has three dimensions analogous to the three dimensions of space, forming a "six dimensional Euclidean continuum." This in turn provides the basis for his theory of "Eternal Recurrence" which attempts to explain experiences of *déjà vu* and the concept of reincarnation. He argues that time curves back upon itself, and so the moment of death is also the moment of (re-)birth. Ouspensky has been criticized for his pseudo-scientific assertion of speculative thinking: nevertheless, he had some original ideas. *Tertium Organum* (1912) is his "reply" to Aristotle's *Organum* and Bacon's *Novum Organum*. IMCF

7   Wilhelm Reich (1897-1957), Austro-Hungarian-born U.S. psychoanalyst. In his *The Function of the Orgasm* (1927) he stressed the need for sexual fulfilment to achieve personal wholeness. Because of his frank and outspoken approach to sex he was ostracized by the psychoanalytical community. In *Character Analysis* (*Charakteranalyse*, 1933, English ed. 1945) he argued that unexpressed emotions are stored in distortions of the muscular system ("body armouring") which prevents the individual from resolving neuroses. JMOF

8   The New School for Social Research was founded in 1919 in New York by the intellectual circle of *New Republic*. It was designed as "a continuous education for the educated." The economist Alvin Johnson was chief director 1921-1946: he was an admirer of John Dewey's theories of education. Johnson was associate editor of the *Encyclopedia of the Social Sciences* (1930), recognized at the time as one of the most important scholarly publications since World War I: his work on the book prepared the ground for what would become the New School's famous social sciences department which fused the German tradition of Simmel and Weber with Dewey and the Chicago Group of sociologists. Foreseeing the treatment of Jews and intellectuals by the Nazis, Johnson encouraged German scholars to emigrate, guaranteeing them faculty positions. The curricula encompassed the social sciences, the humanities, arts and the natural sciences, and the teaching was exploratory and anti-authoritarian, encouraging active, experiential learning. The School has continued, despite financial difficulties, to promote

democratic and cosmopolitan values. The composer John Cage taught at the School for many years, and the nucleus of his 1958 class went on to form the influential Fluxus group of artists who broke interdisciplinary boundaries, challenged the notion of "self-expression," employed chance procedures and parodied consumerism. IMCF

9   José de Rivera (1904-1985), U. S. sculptor. Inspired by the Russian mathematician and physicist Hermann Minkowski's theory of the inseparability of space and time, de Rivera made sculptures which rotate very slowly, moving through space and time simultaneously. His elegant steel and aluminium pieces, polished repeatedly to a brilliant gleaming surface with jeweller's rouge, twist and turn and loop back upon themselves. "Flight" was installed at Newark Airport (1938), and his steel reliefs acclaimed at the New York World's Fair (1939). His sculpture "Infinity" (1966) stands in front of the Smithsonian Institute, Washington D. C. IMCF

10   The Sapir-Whorf hypothesis was developed by Edward Sapir (1884-1939), and Benjamin Lee Whorf (1897-1941), both U. S. linguists. Also known as the Whorf hypothesis it proposes that the structure of a language conditions the way in which the speaker thinks. Whorf: "Certain ways of thinking about the world are made easier than others by the sentence structures of particular languages." Whorf contrasted the world view of the Hopi Indians with that of the "standard average European," conditioned by centuries of Aristotelian logic, which itself was the product of the language structures of ancient Greek and Latin. The hypothesis states that the way in which one thinks is in part conditioned by the way one's language structure enables one most easily to think: different languages induce different ways of envisaging the world. Whorf's work is an important corrective to the assumption that we all live in "the same world" and think about that world in a similar way. Followers of Whorf have claimed that one can only think on the lines laid down by one's language, but this goes further than Whorf intended. The hypothesis is still much debated. Publications include: *Language, Thought and Reality: Selected Writings of Benjamin Lee Whorf* (1951) and *Selected writings of Edward Sapir in Language, Culture and Personality* (1949). IMCF

11   Ira Progoff, depth psychologist. Author of *The Symbolic and the Real* (1963), a description and discussion of the elemental symbols of the psyche, *Depth Psychology and Modern Man* (1959), *Jung, Synchronicity and Human Destiny* and *Jung's Psychology and Its Social Meaning*. A well-known essay "The Integrity of Life and Death", published in *Eranos-Jahrbuch* (1964), is about the assassination of John F. Kennedy and "the Symbolic Dimension of History." IMCF

12 Horace Meyer Kallen (1882-?), Professor emeritus, Graduate Faculty of Political and Social Science, New School for Social Research. He taught courses in philosophy, psychology, aesthetics at Harvard, Princeton and the New School. Author of *The Philosophy of William James, Culture and Democracy in the United States, Of Them Which Say They Are Jews, The Book of Job as a Greek Tragedy,* and *William James and Henri Bergson: A study in Contrasting Theories of Life* . Kallen met F. M. Alexander in New York in 1916, had lessons and wrote a sympathetic review of the 1918 edition of *MSI* for the *Dial*. IMCF

13 John Dewey (1859-1952), U. S. philosopher, one of the founders of the philosophical school of Pragmatism and a representative of the progressive movement in U. S. education. Dewey and Alexander met in New York in 1916 and struck a long-lasting friendship. Between 1915 and 1924 Alexander went to the U.S. for 6 months of the year and Dewey had lessons with him then. Dewey wrote the introduction to the revised edition of *Man's Supreme Inheritance* (1918), to *Constructive Conscious Control of the Individual* (1923) and to *The Use of the Self* (1932). Eric D. McCormack's thesis "Frederick Matthias Alexander and John Dewey: A Neglected Influence" (1952) traces in detail the influence of Alexander's technique on Dewey and his writings. Dewey's *Experience and Nature* (1925) is a systematic presentation of the more important aspects of his philosophy and is generally regarded as his magnum opus. JMOF

14 *Freedom and Culture* (1939) by John Dewey was written in view of the increasing totalitarianism in Europe, Russia and Japan. In this book Dewey argues that democracy can only survive by the practice of democracy in all the cultural institutions of a society: religious, scientific, political etc. JMOF

15 Erich Fromm (1900-1980), German-born U.S. psychoanalyst. Fromm approached the practice of psychoanalysis from the standpoint of philosophy rather than medicine. Inspired by fellow neo-Freudians, Karl Marx and humanism, Fromm lent a cultural and social perspective to psychoanalysis by contending that neurosis can result from culturally inspired needs rather than from frustration of biological drives. A profound critic of materialistic values, he argued for a society that fosters meaningful relations and that responds to what he saw as a person's basic need to avoid loneliness. Fromm's twenty books include *Man for Himself* (1947), *The Art of Loving* (1956) and *To Have or to Be* (1976). JMOF

16 *Escape from Freedom* (1941) examines the social psychology of the capitalist state. It was written as a reaction to the rise of Nazism and one of its major themes is the attraction which charismatic leaders and mass movements

hold for the socially deprived. Fromm insists that it is not enough to become free from oppressive forces: the individual must discover how to use this freedom positively. Fromm is an optimist who believes in moral progress and the ability of human beings to transcend their social conditioning. IMCF

17   Allen Walker Read, linguist and an authority on place names in U. S., "The Lexicographer and General Semantics" in A *Theory of Meaning Analysed: Papers from the Second American Congress on General Semantics* (1942). Assistant editor to Sir William Alexander Craigie, A *Dictionary of American English on historical principles* (1936). *Introduction to a Survey of Missouri Place-Names* (1934). IMCF

18   Charlotte S. Read (*née* Suchardt), assistant to Count Alfred Korzybski at the Institute for General Semantics 1939-50. She was secretary of the Board of Trustees and Co-Editor of the General Semantics Bulletin, and a staff member at Institute Seminars. Trained in zoology and education, Read's special interest was in physical education and dance, the development of kinaesthetic awareness and the holistic approach to personal growth and integration. She was a contributor to *Communication: General Semantics Perspectives* (Lee Thayer, ed.) and her essay "Basic Korzybskian Orientations in the Organizing of Experience" is published in *Coping with Increasing Complexity: Implications of General Semantics and General Systems Theory* (1974, D. E. Washburn and D. R. Smith, eds.). IMCF

19   Marjorie Mercer Kending, teacher of semantics. Research at Columbia University, 1935, on the application of a method for scientific control of the neuro-linguistic and neuro-semantic mechanisms in the learning process. Compiled and edited *Congress on General Semantics: Papers from the Second American Congress on General Semantics, University of Denver, August 1941; non-Aristotelian methodology (applied) for sanity in our time* (1943) and prepared a selection of papers from the Third Congress, 1949. IMCF

20   The Institute of General Semantics was founded in 1938 by Count Alfred Korzybski (*see* note 4). The Institute, based in Lakeview, Connecticut, is dedicated to linguistic research. Since the 1970s the Institute of General Semantics has worked closely with the Society for General Systems Research, in Washington D. C., the largest international professional society devoted to organizing and unifying knowledge. IMCF

21   "The Intensive Journal" is a method of writing and recording subjective feelings, states of mind, memories, attitudes, dreams, fears, aspirations. It is a transpsychological technique for creative and spiritual development. Progoff had used a "psychological workbook" as a psychotherapist in private practice in 1957, which he describes in *The Symbolic and The Real* (1963).

Inspired by Emerson's essay on self-reliance ("Nothing can bring you peace but yourself"), Progoff wished to develop "an instrument capable of mirroring the inner process of the psyche" which people could use *themselves*, without the intervention of an analyst or therapist. The Intensive Journal was formulated at the Eranos Conference in Switzerland in 1965 and designed in 1966; it is registered as part of The Personal Growth and Creativity Program of Dialogue House Associates, Inc., New York (© 1968 and 1974). A person who attends a Dialogue House Journal Workshop receives a registered and numbered copy of the Intensive Journal to be kept permanently and privately at this and other group meetings. A facsimile is printed as an appendix to Ira Progoff's *At a Journal Workshop* (1975) so that the reader can become familiar with the principles and format of the Journal. The technique is associational and creative rather than analytical or diagnostic. IMCF

22   Alfred Schütz (1899-1959), U. S. German-born sociologist and phenomenologist, emigrated to U. S. from Germany in the 1930s. He joined the New School for Social Research in 1941, and became in 1956 full-time Professor of Philosophy and Sociology at the Graduate Faculty. He taught concepts of phenomenology relevant to the social sciences, and created a department of phenomenology and a Husserl Archive at the New School. His *Collected Papers*, published in three vols: I—*The Problem of Social Reality* (1962), II—*Studies in Social Theory* (1964) and III—*Studies in Phenomenological Philosophy* (1966). Schütz was influenced by Henri Bergson, Georg Simmel and William James and wrote on the latter's concept of the stream of consciousness. He believed that social theory must be based upon a foundation of philosophy, and his work combines the sociological methodology of Max Weber with the phenomenological analysis of Husserl. IMCF

23   Paul Rand (1914-), U. S. commercial artist and graphic designer, author of *Thoughts on Design* (1947) and *A Designer's Art* (1985), both illustrated by the author. Rand's offset lithographic images show a sophisticated use of modernist collage and graphic techniques in the context of advertising. Two of his commercial works are in the Museum of Modern Art, New York: "El Producto: every cigar says 'Merry Christmas'" (1954) and "The Pride of 1949: the Kaiser-Frazer Corporation" (1949). Rand took as his maxim Goethe's line: "The hardest thing to see is what is in front of your eyes." IMCF

24   George Ellett Coghill (1872-1941), U.S. professor of biology, embryology and anatomy, he worked mainly at the Wistar Institute of Anatomy and Biology, Philadelphia. In 1928 he delivered three lectures, *Anatomy and the Problem of Behaviour*, in London. Coghill makes a distinction between a "total pattern" and a "partial pattern" of an organism's behaviour, the partial pattern reacting within and subject to the total pattern of an organism's response. Total pattern integrates partial patterns—reflex actions which, if

not co-ordinated, could interfere with each other and lead to conflict. He suggests that the process of inhibition precedes posture which again precedes action, and, if maintained, secures co-ordination and integrity of the whole organism. In 1937 Dr. Peter Macdonald wrote to the *British Medical Journal* that Coghill's anatomical work on the large American type of newt, Amblystoma, provided scientific confirmation of Alexander's discovery of the primary control. In acknowledging *MSI* and *CCCI* which Alexander sent Coghill in 1939, Coghill wrote: "I am reading these with a great deal of interest and profit, amazed to see how you, years ago, discovered in human physiology and psychology the same principles which I worked out in the behaviour of lower vertebrates." When Alexander, because of the war, found it necessary to move himself and his school for children to Stow, Massachusetts (July 1940), he visited Coghill in Florida. Coghill found Alexander's lessons in the Technique a revelation and paid tribute to Alexander in his appreciation in *UCL*. Their last meeting took place a few weeks before Coghill's death in July 1941. JMOF

25   Philomene (Doley) Barr, (*née* Dailey), U. S. teacher of the Alexander Technique. She trained with A. R. Alexander in Massachusetts in the early 1940s. In 1944 she started a class based on Alexander's principles in the Media Friends School in Philadelphia, Pennsylvania. She was founding member, with Mrs. Esther Duke, of The Alexander Foundation in 1946 and its first director. The Foundation ran a school for children at least until 1951. JMOF

26   Francis Otto Matthiessen (1902-1.4.1950), U. S. writer and teacher. Apart from *The James Family* (1947) he published three books on Henry James, Jr. JMOF

27   Henry James, Sr. (1811-82), U. S. philosophical theologian, the father of the novelist Henry James and of the philosopher William James. Henry, Sr., studied at Princeton Theological School (1835-37) but, influenced by Sandemanism, rejected institutional religion. During his many travels in Europe he came across the writings of the Swedish mystic Emanual Swedenborg in 1844, which provided a framework for his own philosophy. JMOF

28   Rabbi Joachim Prinz (1902-), German author of *Jüdische Geschichte* (1931), *Wir Juden* (1934), *Die Reiche Israel und Juda* (1935), *Das Leben im Ghetto* (1937). Prinz was one of the first Jewish leaders to speak out against Nazism and to urge Jews to migrate to Palestine. He was expelled from Berlin and emigrated to U. S. in 1937 where he became Rabbi of Temple B'Nai Abraham, Newark, from 1937, and President of the American Jewish Congress, 1958-66, elected honorary president when he retired. In 1963 he

was one of the ten founding chairmen of the March on Washington. *The Secret Jews* (1973) is a study of the history of Jews in South America, Spain and Portugal. IMCF

29   Ernest Bevin (1881-1951), British Statesman, Foreign Secretary in Labour Government under Clement Attlee, 1945-51. Binkley's remark may be understood in the context of the 4th NATO Council meeting held in London at the beginning of May 1950. Bevin and the American Secretary of State Dean Acheson pressed for Germany to be made a member of NATO as part of the defence of Western Europe against the possible threat of Soviet military action. In 1946 Russian troops had moved towards Tehran until the U. S. warned of repercussions, and Bevin, Churchill and others believed that Stalin was intent upon expanding Soviet power. IMCF

30   Arvid Brodersen (1904-?), sociologist, professor, Graduate Faculty of Political and Social Science, New School for Social Research. Brodersen joined the New School after appointments at the Social Science Department, UNESCO, Paris and the University of Oslo. Author of *Thorstein Veblen as Sociologist, Science and Politics in Max Weber, U. S. Foreign Policy, The Political Elite*, and many articles. Brodersen edited volume II of Alfred Schütz's collected papers, *The Problem of Social Reality* (1964). IMCF

31   Holbrook Jackson (1874-1948), British author, editor and journalist. An expert on industrial design, he was editorial director to the National Trade Press, Ltd. He wrote about the Arts and Crafts movement, Bernard Shaw, Omar Khayyám. *The Anatomy of Bibliomania* (1931), modelled upon Burton's *Anatomy of Melancholy* (1621), and *The Fear of Books* (1932) show his great erudition and wit. *The Eighteen Nineties: a Review of Art and Ideas at the close of the Nineteenth Century* (1913) deals with decadence and dandyism, life lived as a work of art, ornamentalism, the Celtic Renaissance, the revival of fine printing. There are individual chapters on Wilde, Beardsley and Shaw. Jackson sees the artists and writers of the period as both "degenerate and regenerate," embodying, like the romantics before them, both the revolt against subservience to reason and the attempt to create a new mode of living. He considers the Decadents' pursuit of an ideal, sensual existence to be "anything but melancholy or diseased": rather, it was a process of profound personal development and fulfilment. Wilde and Beardsley's conversation is described in this context. Jackson lists four characteristics of the decade: "(1) Perversity, (2) Artificiality, (3) Egoism and (4) Curiosity." (p. 76). He writes that these qualities "are not at all inconsistent with a sincere desire…to expand the boundaries of human experience and knowledge." (p. 76). IMCF

32   Oscar (Fingal O'Flahertie Wills) Wilde (1854-1900), Irish playwright, nov-
      elist, poet and wit. Known especially for *The Picture of Dorian Gray* (1891),
      Lady Windermere's Fan (1892), *Salomé* (1894), *The Importance of Being
      Earnest* (1895), *The Ballad of Reading Gaol* (1894), *De Profundis* (1897).
      Wilde disliked argument and earnestness and delighted in the recondite
      and paradoxical. He excelled at telling stories, both memorized and spon-
      taneously developed, but he was not an egotist who ignored others. His
      conversation had great intellectual and emotional range, and he employed
      calculated pauses and nuances, physical gestures and a mellifluous, velvety
      voice in his performances of an artistically-created and cultivated persona,
      "himself." He mixed fun and profundity, aphorisms and fantastically con-
      voluted stories, truth and fiction. He often appeared surprised and delighted
      by his own words: he desired to amuse and captivate both his audience and
      himself. Wilde claimed that "conversation should touch on everything, but
      should concentrate itself on nothing." At the same time, his conversation
      could be profound and moving and the parables he told were prophetic of
      his tragic destiny. IMCF

33   Aubrey (Vincent) Beardsley (1872-1898), English artist, illustrator and
      author of the erotic romance *Under the Hill*. He is famous for his elegant
      stylized black and white drawings for the periodicals *The Yellow Book*, *The
      Studio* and *The Savoy*. His work is exquisite and refined, a fantasy on notions
      of 17th and 18th Century courtly pleasure and intrigue. His eight pen-and-
      ink drawings for the *Lysistrata* of Aristophanes (1896) and his illustrations
      to Pope's *Rape of the Lock* (1896) are among his most extraordinary crea-
      tions. Holbrook Jackson quotes the critic Arthur Symons on Beardsley's
      conversational manner: "His conversation had a peculiar kind of brilliance,
      different in order but scarcely inferior in quality to that of any other contem-
      porary master of that art; a salt, whimsical dogmatism, equally full of con-
      vinced egoism and of imperturbable keen-sightedness. Generally choosing
      to be paradoxical and vehement on behalf of any enthusiasm of the mind,
      he was the dupe of none of his own statements, or indeed of his own
      enthusiasms, and, really, very coldly impartial." (*The Eighteen Nineties*, p.
      116). Like Wilde's, Beardsley's conversation was informed by his literary
      erudition and his arcane knowledge. IMCF

34   Georg Simmel (1858-1918), German sociologist, author of *Soziologie,
      Untersuchungen über die Formen der Vergesellschaftung* (1922). Simmel stud-
      ied the influence of city life on human behaviour. He believed that the
      individual developed impersonality and reserve as protection against an
      increasingly demanding and complex social hierarchy, concealing emo-
      tions and developing strategies for personal advancement within the sys-
      tem. For Simmel, the social group is formed by individuals who give up only
      a part of their personalities: they are actors, and fragments not only of society

but of themselves. Simmel wrote about social groupings, interactional relations, the intersection of social circles: that artificial world of disguise and self-interest, fear and loneliness, where job, status, class, wealth and image are all that count. IMCF

35 Thomas Hobbes (1588-1679), English political philosopher, author of the great work of political theory, *Leviathan, or the Matter, Forme, and Power of a Commonwealth Ecclesiastical and Civil* (1651). Hobbes saw nature as continual struggle and war, and deduced that society must obey an absolute sovereign authority, so long as that authority can demonstrate its power. Men in their natural state are warring beasts and only the domination of the masses by a powerful elite, headed by the King, can prevent civil disorder, violence and chaos. The book was denounced by both Anglicans and Levellers and as late as the year of Hobbes' death, copies of *Leviathan* were publicly burned in Oxford. IMCF

36 Carl Mayer (1902-74), Sociologist and teacher—he was the foremost expert of his time on the sociologist Max Weber (1864-1920). He was educated at Heidelberg where he wrote his thesis "Church and Sect" under the supervision of Karl Jaspers. He taught the sociology of religion at the New School for Social Research for 30 years, and also took courses in comparative social-political history. His class "Sociology of Modern Anti-Semitism" included the study of ethnicity, society and ideology. Mayer's status at the new School was based upon his reputation as a teacher, in particular his elucidation of Weber's ideas, which helped to define the ethos of the New School in the 1950s. IMCF

37 Guglielmo Ferrero (1871-1942), Italian historian and critic, author of books on Italian history, especially ancient Rome, and the rise of fascism in contemporary Italy. In the 1890s he was described as a socialist, and criticised for praising the superiority of Anglo-Saxon over Latin culture. In 1911, with prophetic insight, he attacked Italian imperialism as being "the mark of a typically German power politics" and urged Italy to renounce her idea of being a world power. In 1925, after signing an anti-fascist manifesto, his mail, critical of Mussolini, was intercepted, and he was placed under house arrest. His many books include *The Greatness and Decline of Rome*, in 5 vols. (1907-09), *Four Years of Fascism* (1924), *The Unity of the World* (1931), *The Principles of Power: the great political crises of history* (1942). IMCF

38 Nathanael West (1904-40), U. S. novelist and satirist of American mass culture. *Day of the Locust* (1939) is his masterpiece. The isolated individual in "the lonely crowd" is drawn to the vicarious illusions of cinema and stardom, and ends by witnessing mass destruction. West was Jewish and had lived in Europe in the 1930s; the fascist crowd hostile to the individual

informs his depiction of Los Angeles, where the mob takes its revenge on the Hollywood dream. Binkley suggests including this crowd scene in a literary-sociological anthology, but for some time sociologists had avoided literary sources in their attempt to make sociology more scientific. IMCF

39 James Boswell (1740-1795), Scottish biographer of Dr. Johnson (1709-1784, English Man of Letters). Boswell's *London Journal: 1762-63* was discovered in 1930-31 and first published in 1950. It is a diary of 18th century London life: coffee houses and theatres, politics, society, prostitution and literary matters. Binkley's comments on the "immortal" Boswell are very appropriate. On 16th July 1763 Boswell wrote: "And, now, O my journal!...Shalt thou not flourish tenfold?" He attached great importance to his unpublished manuscripts and wished them published, believing that they were a contribution to "the history of the human mind." Professor Chauncey B. Tinker, a Boswell scholar, wrote in 1922: "his chosen life work was defeating the forces of oblivion." Binkley's entry for December 2, 1952, suggests the influence of Boswell. IMCF

40 *An Essay on Man, Epistle ii* (1733) by Alexander Pope:
"Know then thyself, presume not God to scan,
The proper study of mankind is man." IMCF

41 Quotation from "Meditation XVII" by the English Metaphysical poet John Donne (1571?-1631): "No man is an *Island*, entire of itself; every man is a piece of the *Continent*, a part of the *main*..." IMCF

42 An "old-fashioned" (U. S. origin) is a cocktail consisting principally of whisky, bitters and sugar served with ice. JMOF

43 Alexander von Schelting, (1894-1963), German scholar who taught in Germany before World War II. He was a noted authority on the sociologist Max Weber (1864-1920) and his principle of Wertfreiheit ("freedom from values"), the ability of the sociologist to objectively describe subjective meanings. Von Schelting wrote *Max Webers Wissenschaftslehre: das logische Problem der historischen Kulturerkenntnis, die Grenzen der Soziologie des Wissens* (1934), and *Russland und Europa im russischen Geschichtsdenken* (1948). IMCF

44 John Skinner (1912-1992), Australian teacher of the Alexander Technique. After service in the Royal Australian Air Force he came to London in 1946. He trained with F. M. Alexander 1947-51? and worked as F. M.'s secretary until F. M.'s death. He continued to work on the teacher training course in Bainbridge St. until 1960, thereafter teaching privately. JMOF

45   William Temple (1881-1944), British churchman, Archbishop of Canter-
      bury (1942-44). A conservative Christian but politically of socialist orien-
      tation. His broad-minded idealism is expressed in *Nature, Man and God*
      (1934) and *Christianity and Social Order* (1942). He started having lessons
      with F. M. Alexander in the early 1930s. JMOF

46   Sir (Richard) Stafford Cripps (1889-1952), British politician. A lawyer,
      Cripps entered Parliament in 1931 as a left-wing Labour MP, antiwar and
      pro-Soviet. He served as ambassador to Moscow (1940-42) and later served
      in Winston Churchill's wartime cabinet. As Chancellor of the Exchequer
      (1947-50), he presided over the post-war austerity program. Cripps and his
      wife, Dame Isobel, started having lesson with F. M. Alexander in 1937 or
      1938. Dame Isobel Cripps later became the matron of the Re-education
      Centre, also known as the Isobel Cripps Centre Ltd., in Holland Park,
      London, which was run by one of Alexander's teachers, Charles Neil, until
      1959. JMOF

47   George Bernard Shaw (1856-1950), Irish satirical dramatist, literary critic
      and socialist propagandist, winner of the Nobel Prize for Literature in 1925
      (which he refused). He was a bold art, music and theatre critic, a prodigious
      pamphleteer, a trenchant essayist on politics, economics and sociology, a
      captivating orator and a prolific letter writer. As a vegetarian and a Socialist,
      a visionary and metaphysician, a sharp observer and critic of classes and
      manners he brought into his writings the debate of moral and intellectual
      conflict with a buoyant wit. Major dramatic works include *You Never Can
      Tell* (1899), *Caesar and Cleopatra* (1901), *Man and Superman* (1905),
      Pygmalion (1913), *Heartbreak House* (1920), *Saint Joan* (1923). JMOF

48   The quote is from The Epistle of Paul the Apostle to the Romans 7:19: "For
      the good that I would I do not: but the evil which I would not, that I do."
      (King James Bible). "The good which I want to do, I fail to do; but what I
      do is the wrong which is against my will;" (New Bible, 1949). Verse 15 is
      similar. JMOF

49   "Cheiro" Count Louis Hamon (1866-1936), expert in the history and prac-
      tice of palmistry. Politicians, royalty, artists, writers and famous figures of the
      day consulted Cheiro at his London salon. He was also a numerologist and
      astrologer, and his predictions proved to be astonishingly accurate: he cor-
      rectly predicted Queen Victoria's date of death and the assassination of the
      Czar. Cheiro was a shrewd observer of human personality "types", and his
      great knowledge of occult history along with his cultivation of high society,
      made him extremely successful. IMCF

50   Albert Redden Alexander (1873-1947), Australian teacher of the Alexander Technique and brother to F. M. Alexander. After service in the Boer War A. R., as he was called, joined F. M.'s teaching practice in 1901 in Melbourne which he continued after F. M. moved to London in 1904. A. R. followed F. M. to London sometime between 1907 and 1910. In 1917 he was paralysed for about six months from a riding accident but recovered, though from then on he walked with a cane and would often sit while teaching the Technique. Between 1915 and 1925 he regularly visited and taught in the U. S. and in 1933 he moved to Boston. He returned to England in 1945 where he died in 1947. JMOF

51   Max Eastman (1883-1969), U. S. journalist and newspaper editor, author and poet, and historian of socialism. In *Heroes I Have Known* (1942) and *Great Companions* (1959), Eastman recalls his friendships with the famous: Hemingway, Chaplin, Russell, Freud, Dewey, Einstein, Trotsky, etc. These memoirs reveal the human qualities beneath the images of celebrity, and they are also concerned with the nature of memory itself. The profile *John Dewey: My teacher and Friend*, from which Binkley is quoting, appears in both books. The sentence preceding Binkley's quotation is: "He [John Dewey] got into a state of tension that in most people would have been an illness. In this emergency he had recourse to ..." IMCF

52   The preceding sentence is: "It is a curious anomaly that acceptance of the theory and practice of non-doing should be comparatively easy in attempts to help the self in external activities, but so difficult in similar attempts connected with internal activities. Such help involves a form of non-doing which must not be confused with passivity..." (*UCL*, p.107) JMOF

53   "To die, to sleep—
      No more, and by a sleep to say we end
      The heartache and the thousand natural shocks
      That flesh is heir to—'tis a consummation
      Devoutly to be wished."
      From Shakespeare's *The Tragedy of Hamlet Prince of Denmark* (written c. 1598), Act III, Scene 1. JMOF

54   Joseph Rowntree (1836-1925), British businessman and philanthropist; director of the family company trading in cocoa and confectionery. His daughter, Agnes Julia, married Dr. Peter Macdonald. In *UoS*, p. 58, F. M. Alexander mentions in a footnote that Joseph Rowntree, after a lesson, described the Technique as "reasoning from the known to the unknown, the known being the wrong and the unknown being the right." The phrasing "pass from the known to the unknown" is featured on the same page. The former quotation is also featured in *UCL*, p. 173. JMOF

55   In 1931 Japanese troops invaded the Chinese province of Manchuria where Britain had commercial interests. China appealed to the League of Nations which failed to take effective action, revealing the inability of Britain and France to act as world powers: both countries were preoccupied with the economic depression in the West, and the Japanese invasion coincided with devaluation in Britain and cuts in expenditure on the Royal Navy. In 1932 the Japanese attacked Shanghai and once again the League was unable, and unwilling, to intervene. The Japanese delegate to the League's meeting in Geneva, Mr. Sato, said that "If we condemned aggressive acts today, it would be necessary to condemn similar acts of other powers against China…before," referring to the history of British exploitation of the Chinese, and warning that any British action against Japan would be seen as hypocritical. The League was discredited in 1935 when Italy invaded Ethiopia. Alexander's comment may be understood in the context of this paralysis of collective action by the Western powers, and in particular the British Government's complete failure of will and political foresight. There was a racist attitude behind this reluctance to intervene: for over a century the British had shared Mr. Sato's view that if China had been "a civilised state, our conduct might have been different." IMCF

56   Bowel movement.

57   Alexander quoted this paragraph in the first chapter of *The Use of the Self* in which he included the next two lines: "… the beauty of the world! the paragon of animals!" From Shakespeare's *The Tragedy of Hamlet Prince of Denmark* (*c.* 1598), Act II, Scene 2. JMOF

58   Sir (Robert) Anthony Eden, first Earl of Avon (1897-1977), British statesman. Foreign Secretary under Neville Chamberlain 1935, resigned 1938. War Minister and Foreign Secretary under Winston Churchill until the Conservative defeat of 1945. Foreign Secretary under Churchill 1951-55. Prime Minister 1955-57. Binkley is referring to a United Nations Assembly meeting in Paris in November, the first month of the 1951-55 Churchill Administration, at which Eden declared that the road to peace lay in "preparation, conference and agreement: starting from small issues and working to the great." IMCF

59   *The Human Use of Human Beings: Cybernetics and Society* (1950) by Norbert Wiener, Professor of Mathematics at the Massachusetts Institute of Technology. The term "cybernetics" (from the Greek "steersman") was chosen in 1947 by Wiener and Dr. Arturo Rosenblueth to describe the field of research concerned with communication and control in machine and animal systems. A comparison of Cybernetics and General Semantics is valid:

both study sensory input and behavioural output between the human being and the environment. Further, General Semantics attempts to create a unified evaluating-communicating structure allowing man to relate to the vast complex of communication systems around him (Korzybski called this structure and process "timebinding") whilst cybernetics monitors the ever-increasing complexity of communications between man and machine, machine and man, machine and machine. General Semantics employs isomorphic correspondences between the person and the world and in cybernetics "the living individual and the operation of some of the newer communication machines" are seen as "precisely parallel." Both disciplines are concerned with the interaction of the human being and man-made systems: Wiener refers to this as "feedback," Korzybski calls it "the structural differential." Binkley suggests a correspondence between Cybernetics and the Alexander Technique. Wiener believed that by demonstrating the similarities between the machine and "the human mechanism," he would make people more conscious of their physical actions and performance: "In both the animal and the machine this performance is made to be effective on the outer world. In both of them their performed action on the outer world and not merely their intended action, is reported back to the central regulatory apparatus. This complex of behaviour is ignored by the average man, and in particular does not play the rôle that it should in our habitual analysis of society." (p. 15). In Cybernetics "feedback increases the stability of performance," and in General Semantics habits of thought are demon-strated and overcome: like the Alexander Technique, these disciplines have an educational and preventive value. Wiener: "If I pick up my cigar, I do not will to move any specific muscles. Indeed in many cases, I do not know what those muscles are. What I do is turn into action a certain feed-back mechanism; namely, a reflex in which the amount by which I have yet failed to pick up the cigar is turned into a new and increased order to the lagging muscles, whichever they may be. In this way, a fairly uniform vol-untary command will enable the same task to be performed from widely varying initial positions, and irrespective of the decrease of contraction due to fatigue of the muscle." (p.14). Wiener's other books include *Cybernetics: or Control and Communication in the Animal and the Machine* (1948), his autobiography *I am a Mathematician* (1956) and *Cybernetics of the Nervous System* (1965, Wiener and J. P. Schade, eds.). IMCF

60   Eugéne Delacroix (1798-1863), French painter of the Romantic period, famous for his works *The Massacre of Chios* (c. 1823), *The Death of Sardanapalus* (1826), *The Women of Algiers* (1833), and *Liberty Leading the People* (1830). His paintings are characterised by their painterliness and by the violence and sensuality of their subjects. *The Journal of Eugéne Delacroix* first appeared in 1893, compiled by Raul Flat and René Piot from hand-written copies of the diaries, note-book entries and fragments. A new version was issued in

1932, carefully corrected from the original documents by André Joubin: it is 1,438 pages long, in three vols. The 1951 Phaidon version is a selection from those entries concerned primarily with the theory and practice of painting, including Delacroix' influential theories of colour. IMCF

61   *Edouard et Caroline* (1951), directed by Jacques Becker, written by Becker and Annette Wademant, starring Anne Vernon and Daniel Gelin. The film has a slight, tenuous plot: a young pianist quarrels with his wife before an important recital. Becker is primarily concerned with character and changing relationships, which are shown with gentle humour and psychological acuity, "a world of enchantment" (*Times*). IMCF

62   Arnold Schoenberg (1874-1951), U. S. Austrian-born composer, famous for his atonal works. In 1923 he announced his revolutionary "Method of Composing with Twelve Tones which are Related Only with One Another." He began composing his *Gurrelieder* in 1900, though it was not finally scored until many years later. It is a work for tenor, soprano, mezzo soprano, chorus and orchestra, part of Schoenberg's early "romantic" period. IMCF

63   Eric David McCormack (1911-1963?), U. S. Professor of Philosophy and Father of the Catholic Order of St. Benedict. The Doctor of Philosophy thesis "Frederick Matthias Alexander and John Dewey: A Neglected Influence" (1958) investigates "the nature and effect of Dewey's contact with the Alexanders and their work"—in effect, it examines the extent to which Alexander's work influenced Dewey and his philosophy. JMOF

64   The Alexander Foundation was the business name for the teaching practice at 16 Ashley Place after F. M.'s death in 1955. It was run by Patrick Macdonald and Beaumont Alexander, F. M. Alexander's younger brother, until about 1970 when the houses in Ashley Place were demolished. JMOF

65   E.g. "For I know thy rebellion, and thy stiff neck..." (Deuteronomy 31:27) "Notwithstanding they would not hear, but hardened their necks, like to the neck of their fathers, that did not believe in the Lord their God." (II. Kings 17:14) "Lift not up your horn on high, speak not with a stiff neck." (Psalm 75:5) "But they obeyed not, neither inclined their ear, but made their neck stiff, that they might not hear, nor receive instruction." (Jeremiah 17:23) See also II. Chronicles 36:13, Nehemiah 9:16, 17, 29, Proverbs 29:1, Isaiah 48:4, Jeremiah 7:26; 19:15. JMOF

66   Progressive education rejects authoritarian teaching methods and emphasizes the need to learn through experience, relating curriculum to student's interests. The European progressive movement started with Maria

Montessori's (1870-1952) school in Rome in 1907. The emphasis is to attend to the individual growth and development of each child, engage the child in both physical and mental activity, and develop the method of preceding all abstract mental operations with concrete experiential activities. Her view in *Scientific Pedagogy* (1912) is that human knowledge and culture is best acquired through natural processes of biological and psychological growth, development and maturation. Other notable figures of the progressive movement are Rudolf Steiner (first school in 1919 near Stuttgart), Franz Cizek in Vienna (emphasizing free expression in art and craft activities), Jacques Dalcroze (founder of the Eurhythmic movement), and Alexander S. Neill (who started Summerhill in 1923). The progressive movement of the United States was dominated by William James, its "founder", and John Dewey, who developed it systematically in many of his papers and books. Contrary to Montessori's method which assumes a clear separation between subject and object in a fixed external world, James rejected this dualism and operated with a more transient and continuous interaction between the organism and its environment, emphasizing how the individual could learn *how* to learn about his or her environment. Teaching is not the imparting of facts and pre-existing paradigms of knowledge, but an extension of the learning process. By increasing one's sensitivity to experiences, including one's stream of consciousness, all options for actions can be appreciated, alternative choices considered, and appropriate responses made. In *Democracy and Education* (1916) John Dewey argues that passive absorption learning is contrary to democratic processes whereas an active participation education would produce individual critical thinking. Applying his "instrumentalism" to education he argued that a school should be a "social laboratory" where assumed knowledge could be pragmatically tested: if not demonstrably seen to work it should be discarded. Children should be encouraged to follow their "natural" proclivity to inquire, explore and respond creatively. Critics of progressive schools object that the approach relies too much on the child itself to sufficiently challenge and stimulate learning. JMOF

67   Play based upon the novel by the English writer Thomas Love Peacock (1785-1866). *Nightmare Abbey* (1818) is an intellectual comedy and droll satire, with little narrative plot but very amusing dialogue. Peacock is a mischievous but good-natured satirist and cleverly debunks scientists, philosophers, Romantic poets and social theorists. *Nightmare Abbey* parodies the Shelley household, including Byron and Coleridge. IMCF

68   Ray Bethers, author of educational books on art appreciation and pictorial perception. *Art Always Changes: How to understand modern pictures* (1958), *From Eye To Camera* (1951). In *Composition in Pictures* (1949) Bethers contrasts and compares paintings of different schools and periods, and visu-

ally demonstrates principles of symmetry and proportion, multiple view-points, volumetrics, outline, perspective and overlapping planes. IMCF

69   The authorship of this paragraph is not clear as in a previous draft of the diaries it is presented as being part of a letter by Gordon Brinsley to Binkley. JMOF

70   Ben Nicholson (1894-1982), British painter, the most highly regarded abstract artist in Britain between the Wars. He worked in the constructivist tradition and was co-editor of the review *Circle: International survey of Constructivist Art* (1937). Famous for his white reliefs of the 1930s where the circle and rectangle are juxtaposed in raised and sunken relief. Between 1939 and 1959 he lived in Cornwall and echoes of the landscape may be found in his work, despite the classical purity of his geometric forms. IMCF

71   Barbara Hepworth (1903-1975), DBE, British sculptor. Hepworth was the most celebrated woman artist of her generation. She had travelled in Europe before settling in Cornwall in 1939, and had known Picasso and Braque: her work embodies her knowledge of modernism and her experience of the Cornish landscape. She was primarily a carver in wood and stone, known for the fine textured surfaces of her standing forms or menhirs: they are pierced and hollowed, integrating the sculpture with the surrounding land-scape. Author of *A Pictorial Autobiography* (1970). She was married to Ben Nicholson in 1932; they divorced in 1951. IMCF

72   Walter H. M. Carrington (1915-), English teacher of the Alexander Tech-nique. Carrington trained with F. M. Alexander in 1936-39 and worked on Alexander's teacher training course at Ashley Place 1946-55. After Alex-ander's death Carrington carried on the training course, since 1960 in Holland Park, London. JMOF

73   Peter Scott (1918-1978), English teacher of the Alexander Technique. After studying piano with Edward Isaacs and James Ching, and theology and law at Oxford, he started having lessons with F. M. Alexander in 1945 and trained as a teacher of the Alexander Technique in 1946-49. After qualification he taught at 16 Ashley Place until 1967. His started his own teachers' training course in 1969 which he ran until his death. JMOF

74   Peggy Williams, (1916-), English teacher of the Alexander Technique. She trained with F. M. Alexander 1947-51 and continued to teach on Alexan-der's training course until his death and on Walter Carrington's training course until 1973. She presently teaches in London. JMOF

75   William Scott (1913-), Scottish painter. Exhibited at the Whitechapel in 1950 and at the Hanover Gallery 1953 and 1954. Scott believed that "European artists must remain European," but wrote of his visit to New York in 1953: "I was overwhelmed by the size and directness of the new American painting." His work combines the influence of Abstract Expressionism with the French tradition from Chardin to Bonnard. His abstractions of kitchen utensils on a table and boats in harbour, are concerned with the balance and proportion of elements on the picture plane. IMCF

76   Erica Brausen, Founder-Director of the Hanover Gallery, London, famous for its exhibitions of the work of Francis Bacon. Brausen was part of the continental influx of art dealers and publishers who came to London in the 1930s and '40s. The gallery showed important European artists like Giacometti, Vasarely, Arp, etc. Brausen helped to make the London art world more international in its outlook. IMCF

77   *Glensalemdon* was never finished. The title is (almost) an anagram of Glencoe (Illinois) and South Salem (New York). JMOF

78   Terry Frost (1915-), British artist. First abstract paintings 1949. Painter full time in St. Ives since 1957. In 1960 he visited U. S. and met the Abstract Expressionists. His earlier works are notable for their hot colours, bright oranges and yellows, and their loose linear forms. His later paintings employ arrangements of oval shapes and a palette of blues and blacks. As with other St. Ives painters, Frost's work relates to the landscape and to Abstract Expressionism, but his vocabulary and sensibility are unmistakably his own. IMCF

79   The Leicester Galleries championed Henry Moore's work from the 1930s. Along with the Redfern Gallery, it was one of the most well-known and widely based of London's modern art galleries. The critic John Russell has written that "the files of the Leicester Galleries include catalogue prefaces by Sickert, Thomas Hardy, Bernard Shaw, Arnold Bennett, Aldous Huxley, Ezra Pound, and many others." IMCF

80   Victor Pasmore (1908-), British painter, maker of reliefs and teacher. He was admired originally for his delicate, atmospheric Hammersmith landscapes of the 1940s. His "conversion" to constructivist abstract reliefs in 1948 is still considered one of the most dramatic incidents in modern British art, although the process was actually lengthier than supposed, and coincided with his association with many of the other St. Ives artists mentioned by Binkley. His work is marked by its restriction and permutation of an individual vocabulary; this is a scholarly, rational art with a poetic resonance, combining abstract means and natural associations. IMCF

81   John Wells, British artist who moved to St. Ives after the war. The "School of St. Ives" was not a movement in art, nor a homogeneous group, it "embraced the range of aesthetic positions from traditional/academic, to primitive, romantic, constructivist, symbolist, etc." (Peter Fuller). Wells was part of the "younger generation" of St. Ives artists, along with Bryan Winter, Sven Berlin, Denis Mitchell, but his work was influenced by the older artists there: "That exquisite precision of John Wells owes something to Ben Nicholson and Naum Gabo." (Patrick Heron). IMCF

82   Peter Lanyon (1918-1964), painter. He studied at the Euston Road School, but rejected realism and explored constructivist principles at St. Ives where he made painted wooden abstract constructions, some of which he used as maquettes for his paintings. He ran an art school with Terry Frost, St. Peter's Loft, St. Ives, 1957-60. Lanyon's work combines analytic intelligence with exuberant brushwork. His earlier cubist explorations of space gave way to aerial views of the landscape, as seen at speed from a glider. He was killed in a gliding accident in 1964. IMCF

83   Patrick Heron, (1920-), British painter and writer on art. He settled in St. Ives 1956. His abstract paintings began with bars (or "stripes") of colour, but for most of his career he has employed the near-circle or near-square, i.e. geometric shapes which blur into organic form. He is known for the warmth and intensity of his colours, a palette more Mediterranean than British. Heron's colours appear to move back and forth in space, as the artist attempts to paint "a pure aesthetic of sensation." His work, undoubtedly influenced by the Cornish landscape and light, is one of the great achievements of 20th century British art. He was art critic in the 1940s for the *New Statesman* and in the 1950s for *Arts Magazine* (New York). His essays were collected in *The Changing Forms of Art* (1958). IMCF

84   Roger Hilton (1911-1975), English painter. In 1954 Hilton had his second one-man show at Gimpel Fils, London. He lived and worked in London 1930-65, after which he settled in St. Just, Cornwall. Hilton's art is uncategorizable: he is a witty, playful, idiosyncratic and above all exuberant painter whose work is simultaneously elegant, energetic and disturbing. Significantly, given Hilton's comments to Binkley, the critic Charles Spencer has described Hilton's pictures as similar to "Paul Klee's inventive wit with its overtones of deep seriousness." Hilton's paintings relate to some inner drama as shown in the posthumous *Night Letters and Selected Drawings* (1980). IMCF

85   T. S. Eliot (1888-1965), British U. S.-born poet, dramatist and critic. He wrote *The Waste Land* (1922) and *The Four Quartets* (1943). Binkley is referring to a speech by the character Sir Claude Mulhammer which appears

in Eliot's *The Confidential Clerk*. The play had its London opening on 16th September 1953 at the Lyric Theatre. *The Cocktail Party*, which ran from May 1950 to February 1951, had been seen by a million and a half people in Britain and the U.S. by the end of 1952, while three and a half million watched the BBC Television performance in 1952. The play, following Eliot's Nobel Prize of 1948, was a major cultural event of the period. *The Confidential Clerk* has never received the critical or popular response of the earlier play. Both plays are about human misunderstanding, personal revelation and religious redemption. Sir Claude Mulhammer's speech is addressed to the character Eggerson:
"My rule is to remember that I understand nobody
But on the other hand never to be sure
That they don't understand me—a good deal better
Than I should care to think, perhaps." IMCF

86   Paul Klee (1879-1940), German-Swiss painter, draughtsman, etcher, teacher and art-theorist. In 1925, Albert Langen published *Pädagogisches Skizzenbuch*, an extract from lectures Klee gave at the Bauhaus 1921-22. The Bauhaus was the great modernist German school of architecture and fine and applied arts 1919-1933. An English edition was published in 1944 in New York by the Nierendorf Gallery under the title *Pedagogical Sketchbook*. The complete text of Klee's 1921-22 lectures is in *Das Bildnerische Denken* ("The Thought of the Plastic Artist") (1956) edited by Jürg Spiller. Klee used aphorisms in his teaching which cannot be reduced to "instruction": "Art does not render the visible, it renders visible" and "The thought is the father of the arrow: how do I extend the limits of my realm?" At the same time, he attempted to formulate the physical and mathematical laws of nature in relation to human perception, using pointing hands, arrows, sequential shapes, etc. The *Sketchbook* shows Klee's philosophy of form, his lexicon of visual signs and their interpretable meanings, though this vocabulary resists absolute comprehension, just as "Klee's artistic work transcends his teaching by a final degree of intensity which is beyond description or explanation." (Eberhard Roters). IMCF

87   William James (1842-1910), U. S. philosopher and psychologist. With a medical degree and a keen interest in philosophy he pioneered physiological and empirical psychology; with him mainstream psychology ceased to be a branch of philosophy and became a laboratory science. In *The Principles of Psychology* (2 vols. 1890) he outlined the scientific methodology of modern psychology, incorporating biological disciplines; thinking and knowledge are seen as parts of the organism's struggle for survival and adaptation. James expanded on Charles S. Pierce's pragmatism—first outlined in the 1870s—which suggests that ideas and beliefs can be evaluated by noting their practical results. The quality, and ultimately, the value of thought depends on

its effects. The truth content of an idea can be experimentally tested by observing its concrete consequences as experienced by the whole organism. He applied this method to his study of religion in *The Varieties of Religious Experience* (Gifford Lectures 1901-02, published 1902) and devoted several lectures and articles to the subject of pragmatism. James was due to meet F. M. Alexander (see Alexander's preface to the new edition of *CCCI*) but, suffering from a heart condition, he returned from Europe to Quebec in 1910 where he died 26 August. JMOF

88   *Art and Freedom: A Historical and Biographical Interpretation of the Relations Between the Ideas of Beauty, Use and Freedom in Western Civilisation from the Greeks to the Present Day* (1942, 2 vols.) by Horace M. Kallen contends that the creation of beauty "affirms man's freedom within and establishes it without." Kallen links individual artistic expression with democratic values in society. He combines history, aesthetics, psychology, sociology and philosophy in this magnum opus which considers the works of Darwin, Freud, Nietzsche, Tolstoy, Proust, Joyce, Cézanne, among others. IMCF

89   James Harvey Robinson (1863-1936), U. S. historian specializing in European history, and author of *The Mind in the Making* (1921). He was one of the founding members of the New School for Social Research, New York, and its first Director. He lectured there in 1919-21. He met F. M. Alexander in New York in 1916 and had lessons. Enthusiastic about the Technique he wrote an influential review of the 1918 edition of *MSI* entitled "The Philosopher's Stone" in the *Atlantic Monthly* (April 1919). JMOF

90   Victor Francis Calverton (1900-1940), U. S. sociologist and literary critic. He was an authority on sexuality, parenthood and marriage. His books include *The Bankruptcy of Marriage* (1926), *Sex Expression in Literature* (1926), *The Liberation of American Literature* (1932) and *Where Angels Dared to Tread* (1941), the latter on religious and socialist communities in the U. S. With Samuel D. Schmalhauser he edited *Sex in Civilisation* (1929) and *New Generation: The intimate problems of modern parents and children* (1930). IMCF

91   Judith Leibowitz (1920-1990), U. S. teacher of the Alexander Technique. Despite a severe polio attack at the age of 15 she went on to become a chemist before training as a teacher of the Technique with Lulie Westfeldt (1948-50). She was a founding member of the American Center for the Alexander Technique (1964) and taught the Technique at The Juilliard School for Performing Arts for 20 years. She is author (with Bill Connington) of an introductory book on the Technique, *The Alexander Technique* (1990). JMOF

92   Deborah (Debby) Caplan (*née* Frank, 1931). U. S. teacher of the Alexander Technique, trained by her mother, Alma Frank, 1950-53, author of *Back Trouble* (1987), and presently teaching in New York City. JMOF

93   Waldo Frank (1889-1967), U. S. novelist, essayist and social historian. Frank called himself "a philosophical social revolutionary" and he wrote about Marxism, industrialisation, Israel, Cuba and South America. His most well-known novel is *The Death and Birth of David Markand* (1934), about a businessman who radically changes his life as he searches for personal truth and spiritual faith. Other novels include *Rehab* (1922), *Chalk Face* (1924) and *Holiday* (1923), the latter about race problems in the South. He also lectured on modern literature at the New School for Social Research. IMCF

94   Alma Frank (1898-1953), U. S. teacher of the Alexander Technique. Trained with F. M. Alexander 1937-40 and taught until her death in New York City. In 1938 she published in the journal *Childhood Development* (Vol. 9, No. 1), the article "A study in infant development," which makes connections between infant growth and behaviour and G. E. Coghill's work on the mechanism of total integration, R. Magnus' work on the reflexes of anti-gravity muscles and F. M. Alexander's work on the primary control of the reflex action of use. JMOF

95   Wilfred Barlow (1915-1991), British doctor and teacher of the Alexander Technique. He trained (1938-45) with F. M. Alexander while studying medicine. As a principal witness in 1948 he helped Alexander win a case for defamation brought by Alexander against the author of a South African government publication, which had maliciously attacked Alexander and his technique. Barlow ran an Alexander teacher training course (1952-1982) with his wife, Marjory, while working as a doctor, specializing in rheumatology. In 1958 he founded The Society of Teachers of the Alexander Technique with his wife and Joyce Wodeman. He was editor of the Society's *The Alexander Journal*. He wrote an influential book on the Technique from a medical point of view in 1973, *The Alexander Principle*, the success of which was followed up with a collection of articles, *More talk of Alexander* (1978) which he edited. JMOF

96   *Men and Supermen* (1954) by Arthur Hobart Nethercot is a critical examination of Shaw's plays. Shaw had often been accused of "ventriloquism", of creating not characters but mouthpieces for his own opinions, and Nethercot examines such charges in regard to Shaw's character types (the Philistine, the Realist, the Idealist etc.) and racial types (the Irishman, the Jew, the American, etc.). Sexual, professional and ideological types are also analysed

and the book concludes with Shaw's creation of The Superman. Nethercot also wrote *The First Five Lives of Annie Besant* (1960). IMCF

97 Binkley is here referring to Henry James, Jr. (1843-1916), U. S. novelist and critic. During his many travels in Europe—and because of his social nature—he established himself as a significant figure in Anglo-American literary and artistic circles. Major works include *The Portrait of a Lady* (1881), *The Bostonians* (1886), *The Turn of the Screw* (1898) and *The Ambassadors* (1903). From 1898 he would often spend summer in his house in Rye, Sussex, and winter in his flat in Chelsea, London. JMOF

98 Siegfried Giedion (1888-1968), Architectural historian and theorist. *Space, Time and Architecture: the growth of a new tradition* (1941) is a seminal work on architectural structure and visual design in the machine age, based upon lectures given by Giedion at Harvard University 1938-39. He examines the work of architects Frank Lloyd Wright, Walter Gropius and Alvar Aalto and explores the relation of geometric to organic form, systems of modular proportion, urban planning and the individual, science and art in synthesis, the evolution of technology. Giedion's book is influenced by Minkowski's Space-Time theory in which the world is conceived in four dimensions and space and time form "an indivisible continuum." For many years the book was obligatory reading for all students of architecture and the visual arts: it is still considered a classic study of design in modernism. Giedion also wrote *The Eternal Present: the beginnings of art* (1957) and *Architecture, You and Me* (1958). IMCF

99 Ronald Searle, English draughtsman, illustrator, cartoonist, famous for his St. Trinian's books. Searle's work is marked by his sense of English eccentricity. He worked for the News Chronicle and Punch and has published many books including *Hurrah for St. Trinian's, and other lapses* (1948), *Looking at London and People Worth Meeting* (1953), *Searle in the Sixties* (1964), and *The Penguin Ronald Searle* (1960). IMCF

100 Arthur Fisher Bentley (1870-1957) U. S. political scientist and philosopher known for his work in epistemology, logic and linguistics and for his contributions to the development of a behavioural methodology of political science. After graduation and post-graduate work in economics and sociology at Johns Hopkins University (1892-93) Bentley studied briefly with Georg Simmel in Berlin. He received a doctorate in 1895, and studied with John Dewey before becoming a journalist and editor. His major work is *The Process of Government: A Study of Social Pressures* (1908) in which he developed a methodology of behavioural social science research and emphasized the study of overt human activity as the raw material of the political process. Concerned more with methodology than with theory, he saw the study of

manifest behaviour as the way to more profound understanding of human affairs. His attention gradually shifted to epistemology and away from intensive examination of sociology and politics. In *Knowing and the Known* (1949) (with John Dewey) which discusses the problem of knowledge the authors argue that the perceived discontinuity between the "knower" and the "known", which is expressed in familiar dichotomies, like stimulus-response, abstract-concrete, mind-body etc., is at the root of the problem of philosophical inquiry. They suggest a new vocabulary which expresses organism and environment as a unity, separable only by analysis and selective abstraction. Bentley went further than Dewey and postulated complete continuity in his "transactional" view of social explanation, one in which knowledge is seen as a social phenomenon. (This approach is very similar to that of General Semantics, *see* note 5). JMOF

101   Serge Diaghilev (1872-1929), Russian impressario, producer of the Ballets Russes. Binkley is probably referring to photographs by de Meyer, Bert, Balough, Lipnitski, Druet, and E. O. Hoppe of the dancers Nijinsky, Massine, Lopokova, Karsavina, and others. Photographs of Nijinsky in *Petrushka, Le Spectre de la Rose* and *Les Orientales* are the most famous in 20th century ballet. The drawings probably included the exotic costume designs of Leon Bakst. The music must have featured Stravinsky's *L'oiseau de Feu* and his *Le Sacre du Printemps*. IMCF

102   Piet Mondrian (1872-1944), Dutch painter of geometric abstracts. He employed straight horizontal and vertical black lines with rectangles and squares in the primary colours red, yellow and blue. His work developed out of Expressionism and Cubism and is related to the De Stijl movement in architecture: an art of asymmetrical equilibrium and purity of means. Mondrian was a Theosophist and Neo-Platonist searching for a transcendent truth "through the balance of unequal but equivalent oppositions." IMCF

103   Yasuo Kuniyoshi (1893-1953), U. S. figurative artist who emigrated from Japan around 1906. From the mid-1930s he taught art at the New School for Social Research. In 1952 he represented contemporary American art at the Venice Biennale. During World War II Kuniyoshi painted solitary clowns in desolate landscapes and in bombed cities. In the last three years of his life he made a dramatic change to brilliant, strident, dissonant colours, painting carnivals and circuses and masquerades. These are his most original works, brightly coloured and festive, but ominous and melancholy. His posthumous exhibition was held in Tokyo, March 20-April 25, 1954. IMCF

104   Sir Charles (Scott) Sherrington (1857-1952), British physiologist who laid the foundations for an understanding of integrated nervous function in higher animals. He discovered that reflexes do not work in isolation but as

integrated activities of the total organism. His first proof for "total integration" was his demonstration (1895-98) of the "reciprocal innervation" or "antagonistic action" of muscles, also known as Sherrington's Law: when one set of muscles is stimulated, muscles opposing the action of the first are simultaneously inhibited. Sherrington and Alexander first met in the 1920s and although Sherrington did not have lessons he pays a tribute to Alexander in *The Endeavour of Jean Fernel* (1946). The Gifford Lectures he gave in 1936-37 were published as *Man on his Nature* (1940) where he summarises the biological evolution of humankind and its mind, emphasizing the unity of the organism. JMOF

105   Originally the AI (Artists' International) group, founded in 1933 by Misha Black and the architect Cliff Rowe. They were active anti-fascists, took part in strikes and produced a mimeographed newspaper. It became the Artist's International Association in 1935 and defined its philosophy as "conservative in art and radical in politics." It hosted a debate in 1938 between Realists and Surrealists. The AIA occupied various locations around Soho: Charlotte Street, Soho Square, Lisle Street. The political radicalism was not so fierce in Binkley's time, though it was allied to the Ban the Bomb campaigns. Artists shown at the AIA during the 1930s and '40s included Moore, Nicholson and Hepworth. IMCF

106   *George Ellett Coghill—Naturalist and Philosopher* by C. Judson Herrick published by The University of Chicago Press, 1949. The three parts of the book cover 1) Coghill's biographical details, 2) his scientific method and results (on reflex action, inhibition, total and partial patterns, individuation and motivation) and 3) his philosophy of life and science—from transcribed interviews with Herrick. JMOF

107   Sir Julian (Sorell) Huxley (1887-1975), English biologist, author and humanist philosopher. Through his research and writings Julian was influential in shaping the modern development of embryology and studies of behaviour and evolution. His *Evolution: The modern synthesis* (1942) summed up the (still) most favoured hypothesis of evolution: the combination of Darwin's theory of natural selection and Mendel's discovery of the principal workings of genetic inheritance. Julian Huxley was the first director general of UNESCO (1946-48). Despite the enthusiasm of his younger brother, Aldous, for the Technique, Julian did not have lessons. JMOF

108   James Eustace Radclyffe McDonagh (1881-1965), British doctor, professor at the Royal College of Surgeons, 1916; founder and director of the Nature of Disease Institute since 1929. He did research into venereal diseases, the common cold, influenza and corresponding infections in animals. He advocated a varied diet consisting mainly of fresh vegetables, fish and chicken.

Published among others *The Nature of Disease* (3 vols. 1924-27-31)—in the third volume of which he devoted the first chapter, "Mal-co-ordination and Disease," to the Technique—and *The Nature of Disease to Date* (1946). He was F. M. Alexander's doctor and F.M .would refer people who needed medical attention to him. JMOF

109   Anthony Mario Ludovici (1882-1971), British author and Captain in the RFA. He started as an artist, illustrating books, and was for some time private secretary to Auguste Rodin. He translated six vols. of Nietzsche's philosophy and lectured on the subject. He wrote seven novels and 26 non-fiction books on subjects as diverse as Nietzsche, politics, women's studies, childbirth, health and nationalism. A pupil of F. M. Alexander, he enthusiastically advocated the Alexander Technique in his book on the "male sex", *Man: An Indictment* (1927) and his book on health, *Health and Education Through Self-Mastery* (1933). JMOF

110   *A Likely Tale: a Play in Three Acts* by Gerald Savory. First produced at the Globe Theatre, London, March 22, 1956, directed by Peter Ashmore, with Robert Morley as Oswald Petersham and Margaret Rutherford as Mirabelle Petersham. A father threatens to leave his money to the house-maid, and his grandson tries to marry her. A comic drama about disinheritance, with a subplot of romantic intrigue. The play was published in 1957. IMCF

111   *Alexander and the Doctors* is the title of an unfinished typescript by Ron Brown, a pupil and friend of F. M. Alexander. The book was to be based on the South African libel case in which Alexander sued a government magazine for a defamatory article and won substantial damages. The finished book would have included a biography of Alexander, an introduction to the Technique plus summaries of Alexander's four books, the text of the libellous article, the text of the cross-examinations of witnesses in London and a summary of the court proceedings, including summaries of the judgment, the appeal and the appeal judgment. Owing to Ron Brown's premature death the book was never published. Parts of the typescript have since been published on their own. JMOF

112   Paul D. McLean, U. S. professor of neurophysiology. McLean studied Darwinian inheritance in relation to the development of the brain. In *A Triune Concept of the Brain and Behaviour* (1969) he suggests that the brain is triune because it is divided into three parts, each the product of a different stage of evolution. The reptile brain at the base of the brainstem is a reminder of our reptile ancestors, and is enveloped by the paleocortex or limbic system which developed later and determines our emotions; this in turn is surrounded by the neocortex, the grey matter which allowed human beings to develop language and logic. IMCF

Index of Names

INDEX OF NAMES

Page numbers in italics refer to the endnotes. The page number in bold refers to the main endnote entry on the subject. Illustrations are not included in the index.

———